Electromagnetism
AND
RELATIVITY

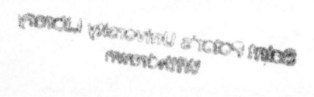

Under the consulting editorship

of Frederick Seitz

Electromagnetism
AND
RELATIVITY

E. P. Ney

Professor of Physics
University of Minnesota

HARPER & ROW, PUBLISHERS

New York and Evanston

The views of space and time which I wish to lay before you have sprung from the soil of experimental physics, and therein lies their strength. They are radical. Henceforth space by itself, and time by itself, are doomed to fade away into mere shadows, and only a kind of union of the two will preserve an independent reality.

H. Minkowski, 21 September, 1908

Contents

Preface

Since 1958, we have had an honors section in second-year physics at the University of Minnesota. This group has been composed of students in the top five percent of their freshman physics and mathematics classes. We have supplemented their modern physics study with a number of "handouts," which discuss certain subjects in more depth than the standard textbooks intended for a first course in contemporary physics. These notes on relativity represent such additional material. I believe that to benefit from these notes all that is required is one year of general physics, one year of calculus, and an open mind.

November 29, 1961   EDWARD P. NEY
Minneapolis, Minnesota

CHAPTER 1. Classical Mechanics and Electromagnetism

In order to understand the significance of the special theory of relativity, we must examine the state of theoretical and experimental knowledge in 1905 when our ideas were greatly broadened and extended by Einstein's spectacular contribution. The theories that formed the foundation of physics at the end of the nineteenth century were classical mechanics as formulated by Newton and the electromagnetic theory of Maxwell. Although kinetic theory was also well developed, we will not review its fundamentals here. Kinetic theory is an important application of the laws of mechanics and statistics to assemblies of atomic particles, and relativity applies to it but only in the sense that relativity applies to all matter in space. The other great theory of the early twentieth century, quantum mechanics, makes itself felt especially on the atomic scale.

CLASSICAL MECHANICS

We shall first investigate the relationship between systems and observers as given by Newtonian mechanics. In this mechanics

1

we shall examine the concepts of space and time and see that a certain restricted form of relativity already existed here.

Newton's first law states essentially the condition for the absence of external forces. This law asserts that there is no difference mechanically between a body at rest and one in uniform motion; both bodies show the absence of external forces. This statement implies, therefore, that there are no preferred or selected systems if we consider only those systems at rest or in uniform motion with respect to one another. These are called *inertial systems*, and in these systems Newton's laws would hold. If we asked what "at rest" means, the Newtonian physicist would probably define at rest as "not in motion with respect to the fixed stars." However, we do not recognize as significant the concept of "absolute rest," and we need only be able to distinguish inertial systems — i.e., systems in which an object at rest remains at rest and an object in uniform motion remains in uniform motion — systems in which Newton's laws hold. In relativity one of these systems may, however, be rather special. The system containing the observer at rest in it is called the *proper system* for that observer, and we shall see that it must be distinguished and identified.

How then do we describe events in these inertial systems, and in fact how do we relate the systems one to the other? What is the meaning of relativity in Newtonian mechanics? We may best begin by recalling a simple experiment. Most of us have experienced the sensation of sitting in a railroad train at rest in the station. Perhaps one dozes for a few moments and awakes to see the train on the next track in relative motion. In such a situation one is completely at a loss to say which train is moving. There is only the observation of relative motion. One cannot decide whether one train or both are moving without looking down at the ground. These are two inertial systems in Newtonian relativity and both are equivalent. An observer in train A says that train B moves in the direction of the $-x$ axis at a speed v; an observer in train B says that train A moves with speed v in the direction of the $+x$ axis. We can go from one description to the other simply by changing the sign of the relative velocity v. It should be pointed out that an observer who was always awake could have perceived which train began moving. During the time that one train accelerated from rest, it was not an inertial system. An alert observer on seeing the relative motion start could have decided by the presence or absence of forces on him whether his train or the other was accelerating. However, after the relative motion has been established, he cannot distinguish between the inertial systems. This is Newtonian relativity.

We must see how to write the transformation mathematically.

We refer to systems Σ and Σ'. The system Σ' moves in the direction of the $+x$ axis with respect to Σ with velocity v. We could equally well say that Σ moves in the direction of the $-x'$ axis with velocity v. Sometimes we may speak of Σ as being at rest, but we must realize that "at rest" has no absolute meaning. The coordinates of a point in Σ are x, y, z; the coordinates in Σ' are x', y', z'. In principle there is a fourth coordinate, time, t and t'. In Newtonian mechanics it is *assumed* that this coordinate has the same value in all systems according to Newton's concept that time passes "uniformly and without reference to any external object whatsoever." The assumption that $t = t'$ is not made in special relativity, and it is the relaxation of this restriction that produces this remarkable theory.

The Newtonian transformation is then

$$x = x' + vt' \quad (1) \qquad x' = x - vt \quad (1a)$$
$$y = y' \quad (2) \qquad y' = y \quad (2a)$$
$$z = z' \quad (3) \qquad z' = z \quad (3a)$$
$$t = t' \quad (4) \qquad t' = t \quad (4a)$$

We assume that the origins of the two systems coincide at

$x = x' = y = y' = z = z' = t = t' = 0$. We can see that the transformation equations are correct by observing in Eq. (1) that the description of the motion of the origin of Σ', i.e., $x' = 0$ is given by $x = vt$. The transformation equations can be converted into each other by exchanging the primed and unprimed quantities and reversing the sign of v. *This is an important property of all relativistic transformations.*

The Galilean transformation equations we have written make Newton's laws *invariant*. When we say that Newton's laws are *invariant under a Galilean transformation*, we simply mean that both observers would write the equation of motion of a particle in the same way. We must show that this is true. We shall carry out this trivial calculation very formally because in special relativity the corresponding kind of calculation is not so obvious.

1. We wish to show that Newton's second law has the same form in all inertial systems. This is equivalent to showing that the acceleration is invariant.

2. Express v_x in terms of v'_x

$$v_x = \frac{dx}{dt} = \frac{dx'}{dt} + v\,\frac{dt'}{dt} = \frac{dx'}{dt'} + v$$

and, therefore,

$$v_x = v'_x + v$$

3. Now differentiate to get a_x in terms of a'_x.

$$\frac{dv_x}{dt} = \frac{dv'_x}{dt} + \frac{dv}{dt} = \frac{dv'_x}{dt'} + 0$$

so

$$\frac{dv_x}{dt} = \frac{dv'_x}{dt'}$$

or

$$a_x = a'_x$$

which is the invariance we wished to prove.

We shall now show a graphical representation of the transformation which will be carried over and modified in relativity. In relativity the graphical picture of the transformation is called a *Minkowski diagram*. Figure 1 shows the transformation and must be studied carefully.

Shown on this diagram are the x, x', t, and t' axes. Note that the t axis is marked $x = 0$. This is the meaning of the t axis in the same way that the y axis in an ordinary x, y coordinate system

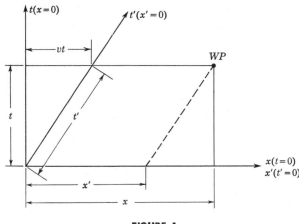

FIGURE 1

really means y axis ($x = 0$). In the same way the other axes are identified for example, the x' axis means ($t' = 0$). The point WP is a *world point*. It represents an event in space time. Its coordinates in Σ are x and t, and its coordinates in Σ' are x' and t'. Note that to find the coordinates the projections are parallel to the axes and that to make $t = t'$ as is required the scale must be different on the t and t' axes. A measure proportional to the unit is the length of the lines to t and t'. It is easily seen that the construction guarantees the Galilean transformation $x' = x - vt$ from the geometry. The motion of an object in space time would be represented by a series of world points in such a Minkowski diagram. Note that the x, t axes need not have been made orthogonal. Any angle would do. Figure 2 shows another possible representation of the world point in the two coordinate systems with no orthogonal axes. As long as the projections to determine x, x', t, t' are parallel to the proper axes, the transformation is guaranteed.

A very important problem in relativity is the synchronization of clocks. We shall discuss this problem from the Newtonian as well as the relativistic point of view. However, to see the steps involved in the process of "setting clocks," we must understand something about the propagation of signals (sound, light) since

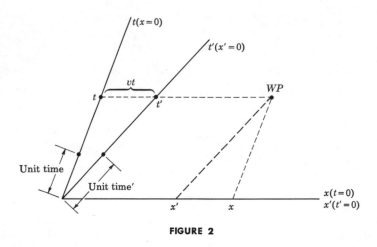

FIGURE 2

these signals are necessary to the synchronization. To state it simply, it is easy to synchronize and compare clocks which are sitting side by side in their own proper system, but unfortunately most clocks are not at the same world point. We shall study this problem in detail, but first we must examine the phenomena of wave propagation.

WAVES

In elementary physics we classify waves as longitudinal and transverse according to whether the vibration takes place in the direction of propagation (longitudinal) or perpendicular to that direction (transverse). Transverse waves may be *polarized* if the vibration takes place in some preferred direction in space. Longitudinal waves by their nature do not have the property of polarization.   A wave in physics is characterized by the following parameters.

1. Velocity of propagation: v.
2. Wavelength λ.

or wave number: $\bar{\nu} = \dfrac{1}{\lambda}$ or $k = \dfrac{2\pi}{\lambda}$.

3. Frequency: f *or sometimes* ν.
4. State of polarization, i.e., *plane, circular, elliptical, unpolarized*.

It is frequently useful to remember that an unpolarized beam may be represented as equal intensities of two incoherent beams of plane polarized light which are polarized at right angles to each other.   The basic states of polarization are plane-polarized and circular-polarized (right or left) light.

5. Amplitude A is maximum displacement in the wave.

6. Intensity I is $\dfrac{\text{energy}}{\text{area time}}$ carried by the wave.

As is well known, the wavelength frequency and velocity are related by $v = \nu\lambda$.   Some examples of waves are the following:

1. Sound in air or perfect liquid (longitudinal).
2. Surface water waves (transverse).   We distinguish between surface tension and gravity waves.
3. String waves (transverse).   These are waves such as are set up in a piano string.
4. Seismic waves (transverse, longitudinal).
5. Electromagnetic waves — light (transverse).   Under electromagnetic waves we include visible light, X-rays, radio waves, infrared, γ-rays, etc.   Figure 3 shows a portion of the spectrum of electromagnetic waves.

All waves except electromagnetic waves require a medium for their propagation.*   Frequently the propagation of waves gives very

---

* De Broglie waves associated with the propagation of matter in vacuum are an exception to this statement.   Since matter may be propagated without a medium, so may De Broglie waves.

important information about the medium. For example, the velocity of sound in air is $v = \sqrt{\gamma RT/M}$. A knowledge of the composition of air determines γ and M; and, therefore, the velocity

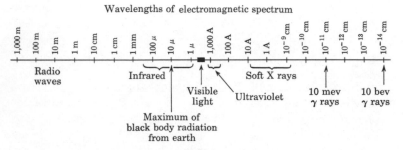

FIGURE 3

of sound may be used to measure the temperature of air. This method has been used with great success at very high altitude by exploding grenades which are flown on rockets. The temperature may be measured by this method even though the pressure is very low.

Another example of the propagation describing the features of the medium is given by seismic waves. In solid matter seismic waves are both transverse and longitudinal; but in a liquid, which cannot support a shear, only longitudinal waves may propagate. A study of seismic waves shows that only longitudinal waves may pass all the way through the earth, and this fact is the strongest experimental evidence that the earth has a liquid core.

PROPERTIES OF WAVES PROPAGATED THROUGH MATERIAL MEDIA

The Velocity of Propagation and the Motion of the Medium

Sound is a typical wave of the sort we are discussing, and we shall use it as an example. When sound is propagated through air at rest, it travels through this air with a velocity $v = \sqrt{\gamma RT/M}$.

However, if the air is moving, it can carry the sound with it. The velocity of propagation is the vector sum of the velocity in still air and the velocity of the air. The report of a distant cannon is heard sooner by an observer if a wind blows from the cannon toward him and later in reverse case. If we use sound waves in experiments to synchronize clocks, we must take this fact into account. In an extreme example, if a wind were blowing from an observer toward a sound source and the wind had the velocity of sound, no sound would reach the observer.

Asymmetrical Doppler Effect

An elementary analysis of the Doppler effect for sound shows that the magnitude of the effect depends not only on the relative velocity of source and observer but upon which is in motion with respect to the medium. The equations are

$$\nu' = \nu \left(1 \pm \frac{v}{s}\right) \qquad \text{OBSERVER IN MOTION}$$

$$\nu' = \nu \, \frac{1}{\left(1 \mp \frac{v}{s}\right)} \qquad \text{SOURCE IN MOTION}$$

where v represents the relative velocity and s the velocity of sound. The two equations reduce to the same value for $v < s$; but with $v \to s$, they give very different answers. In the case of light (which does not require a medium for propagation) the Doppler effect is symmetrical in source and observer motions, i.e., it only depends on the relative velocity.

Dispersion

A very important property of waves propagated through media is the phenomenon of dispersion. The dispersion of waves in a medium leads to the phenomena of absorption, refraction, and the splitting of *phase* and *group* velocities. Again, we shall discuss *non*electromagnetic waves because the understanding of dispersion of electromagnetic waves in dielectric materials requires a very special treatment, which we shall consider later.

By dispersion we mean that the phase velocity of propagation varies for different waves. The most important case of dispersion arises when the velocity of propagation depends on the wavelength. For this discussion we shall use water waves as an example. Our principle objective is to distinguish between phase and group velocity.

Our fundamental starting point is that, in a dispersive medium, waves of different wavelength travel with different speeds. The term *normal dispersion* is used when waves of longer wavelength travel with higher speeds although in physics $dv/d\lambda$ may be either positive or negative depending on the kind of wave and the medium. Figure 4 represents two wave trains of infinite extent (and therefore monochromatic), and the beat pattern which results when the waves are added together at two different times t_1 and t_2. Note that at time t_1, points A and B on the crests of the two waves are coincident and coincident with the maximum of the beat pattern C. At the later time t_2, the point B has moved farther (longer wavelength travels faster) in the direction of propagation than has point A on the shorter wavelength wave. The point C has progressed a shorter distance than either A or B.

The velocities of the points A and B are referred to as the *phase velocity* of these monochromatic waves, and the velocity of C is the *group velocity* of the wave. The group velocity of a wave is usually the observed velocity, and the energy in a wave is transmitted with the group velocity. We now proceed to make Fig. 4 quantitative.

Assume that the amplitudes of the waves are

$$wave\ A: \ y_A = \cos{(kx - \omega t)}$$
$$wave\ B: \ y_B = \cos{[(k + \Delta k)x - (\omega + \Delta\omega)t]}$$

The phase velocity v of either wave may be determined by asking for the condition of a crest or a trough (i.e., fixed phase). For example, for wave A the velocity is given by $kx - \omega t =$ constant. We may take the constant $= 0$ for a wave crest, and we obtain

$$\frac{x}{t} = v = \frac{\omega}{k} = \frac{2\pi f}{2\pi/\lambda} = f\lambda = v$$

Let us now add waves A and B. Simple trigonometry leads to

$$y_A + y_B = 2 \cos \frac{1}{2} (x \, \Delta k - t \, \Delta \omega)$$

$$\times \cos \left[\left(k + \frac{\Delta k}{2} \right) x - \left(\omega + \frac{\Delta \omega}{2} \right) t \right]$$

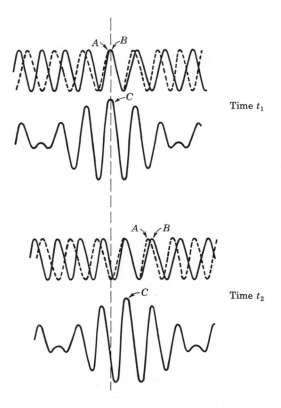

Time t_1

Time t_2

FIGURE 4

The second cosine term is easily recognized as a variation having the average phase velocity. The term $2 \cos \frac{1}{2}(x \, \Delta k - t \, \Delta \omega)$ is the modulation or beat and represents the group motion. Figure 5 shows the sum of y_A and y_B and the appropriate velocities. We can get the group velocity as we did the phase velocity by observing that

$$x\,\Delta k\,-\,t\,\Delta\omega\,=\,0\ \text{crest}$$

and therefore

$$\frac{x}{t}\,=\,\mu\,=\,\frac{d\omega}{dk} \tag{5}$$

The velocity μ is the group velocity.

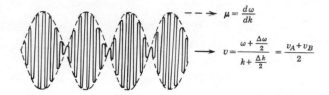

FIGURE 5

If the medium is nondispersive, $\mu\,=\,d\omega/dk\,=\,d(kv)/dk\,=\,v$, and the group and phase velocities are the same. We may put the equation $\mu\,=\,d\omega/dk$ in other forms by observing that $k\,=\,2\pi/\lambda$, $\omega\,=\,kv$

$$\mu\,=\,\frac{d\omega}{dk}\,=\,\frac{d}{dk}\,(kv)\,=\,v\,+\,k\,\frac{dv}{dk}\,=\,v\,-\,\lambda\,\frac{dv}{d\lambda}$$

The expression most frequently used is

$$\boxed{\mu\,=\,v\,-\,\lambda\,\frac{dv}{d\lambda}} \tag{5a}$$

Finally, we give an example of phase and group velocity for water waves.

For surface tension waves (shallow water)

$$v^2\,=\,\frac{2\pi T}{\rho\lambda}$$

where T = surface tension
  ρ = density
  λ = wavelength
  v = velocity

This may be written

$$v = \sqrt{\frac{T}{\rho}} \, k \quad \text{and} \quad \omega = kv = \sqrt{\frac{T}{\rho}} \, k^{3/2}$$

Since $\mu = d\omega/dk$,

$$\mu = \frac{3}{2} \sqrt{\frac{T}{\rho}} \, k^{1/2} = \frac{3}{2} \sqrt{\frac{T}{\rho}} \, k = \frac{3}{2} v$$

In this case the group moves at a speed 1.5 times greater than the phase velocities.

For gravity waves

$$v^2 = \frac{g\lambda}{2\pi}$$

and

$$v = \sqrt{\frac{g}{k}} \quad \omega = kv = \sqrt{kg}$$

$$\frac{d\omega}{dk} = \mu = \frac{1}{2} \sqrt{\frac{g}{k}} = \frac{1}{2} v$$

And in this case the group moves at a speed $\frac{1}{2}$ of the phase velocity.

If one looks at water waves and fixes one's attention on the individual wavelets and the group, the above predictions may be easily verified. In deciding whether the waves are surface tension or gravity waves, it is useful to note that, in water, surface tension waves have wavelengths less than 1.7 cm and frequencies greater than 14 sec^{-1}, whereas gravity waves have wavelengths longer than 1.7 cm and frequencies less than 14 sec^{-1} (see Prob. 1).

This discussion on dispersion may have been overdetailed, but it is important to recognize that a monochromatic wave would have to be of infinite extent and therefore cannot exist. In reality we always observe a group of waves of finite extent propagating signals or energy. Since energy is transmitted with the group velocity, it is important to see its connection with the phase velocity which is frequently important in theory. When we describe particles and waves according to quantum mechanics, we see that the velocity of the wave group describing the particle must be associated with the velocity of the material particle, so again it is the group velocity that has physical significance. In the propagation of light signals through a vacuum we will not need to distinguish between group and phase velocity for experiment has shown no dispersion of light even from the most distant galaxies, and therefore we must conclude that light is propagated in space without dispersion.

Now that we have emphasized the importance of the medium in the propagation of all waves except light, we must face and discuss the problem of the propagation of electromagnetic waves *for which no medium is required*. When a medium is involved, it is easy to see what oscillates in the wave (it is some property of the medium: pressure, displacement of particles, etc.); but it is natural to ask, if there is no medium, what oscillates? To answer this question, we must briefly summarize the electromagnetic theory of light as given by Maxwell.

MAXWELL'S THEORY OF ELECTROMAGNETIC WAVES

In 1873 Maxwell published his *Treatise on Electricity and Magnetism*, which was one of the outstanding contributions to physics and in which he formulated this theory of electromagnetic waves. We shall review here the elementary macroscopic laws of electricity and magnetism and show that they lead to the prediction of electromagnetic waves. In discussing Maxwell's equations, we shall restrict these equations to the description of free-space electromagnetic waves. We must develop the free-space case to see how the existence of electromagnetic waves is consistent with the elementary laws of electricity and magnetism. The laws which Maxwell married in formulating his equations were:*

1. *Gauss' law for electrostatics.* It may be stated "4π lines of force diverge from a unit charge." The electric field **E** is the number of lines of force per square centimeter. The field **E** is also the force on a unit charge in dynes. **E** is a vector quantity.

* In what follows we shall use cgs nonrationalized units (i.e., the same units used by Maxwell and by most physicists). E is in esu, H in oersted, e in esu, j in emu, ($c = 3 \times 10^{10}$ cm/sec).

2. *Gauss' law for magnetostatics.*   No free magnetic poles exist, and, therefore, magnetic lines of force are continuous.   **H** is the magnetic field, the number of lines/cm^2.   It is also the force in dynes on an imaginary unit pole.   It is measured in oersteds.

3. *Faraday's law of induced emf.*   "The induced electromotive force produced by a changing flux is emf $= -1/c(d\varphi/dt)$." The — sign reflects Lenz's law that the emf is generated to oppose the change in flux creating it. φ is the magnetic flux in maxwells, i.e., $\varphi/A = B$ gauss.   The emf is given in esu; this is the reason for the appearance of $1/c$ in the equation.

4. *Ampère's law of magnetism.*   We shall use this in the following form: "The work required to move an imaginary unit magnet pole around a current I is $4\pi I$ ergs." I is measured in emu here.

5. *Maxwell's displacement current.*   If an electric field changes with time, it will create a magnetic field.   If dE/dt is the time rate of change of the electric field, a magnetic field is produced as if there were a current flowing parallel to dE/dt with the displacement current given by $j_D = 1/4\pi c(dE/dt)$. j_D is the displacement current density in emu/cm^2, and E is in dynes/esu. If electrostatic units were used here, $j_D = 1/4\pi(dE/dt)$ with both E and j in esu.   We shall discuss this concept of displacement current in some detail later.

The five laws which we have stated are all that are required for the derivation of electromagnetic waves.   However, for the sake of completeness it should be pointed out that a sixth law is required to describe the motion of charged particles in electric and magnetic fields or in electromagnetic waves.   This is the equation for the Lorentz force on a charge e.

6. *Lorentz force.*   The force on a charge in electric and magnetic fields is

$$\mathbf{F} = e\mathbf{E} + \frac{e}{c}\,\mathbf{v} \times \mathbf{B} \tag{6}$$

The force is in dynes, e in esu, E in esu, and B is in gauss.   In free space $B = H$.   The vector product $\mathbf{v} \times \mathbf{B}$ means that the force has the magnitude $vB \sin \theta$ and the direction obtained by rotating **v** into **B** by the right-hand rule. The force is perpendicular to the plane containing **v** and **B**, and θ is the angle between **v** and **B**.

We shall not make immediate use of (6) but will find it essential in discussing any interaction of fields and charged particles. The combination of laws 1 → 5 into succinct mathematical form is accomplished elegantly by the methods of vector calculus using several famous mathematical theorems. We will not assume a knowledge of these methods; therefore, our derivation of the differential equations must start from first principles and will be formally more cumbersome. The physics of the equations, however, is well-shown by the following treatment. We shall derive from each law the differential equation appropriate to Maxwell's formulation. For those versed in vector calculus, we will simply write the vector equation in the compact notation as well.

Gauss' Law for Electrostatics

Consider a right-handed coordinate system containing an elementary volume dx, dy, dz. This volume is assumed to contain a charge q. We wish to determine the conditions on the components of the electric field E_x, E_y, E_z imposed by Gauss' law.

We consider each face separately and count the number of lines of force entering face A and leaving face B. We subtract to get the net number of lines originating within the box. The lines entering at A are $E_x\,dy\,dz$, and those leaving at B are $E_{(x+dx)}\,dy\,dz$. Since $E_{(x+dx)} = E_x + (\partial E_x/\partial x)\,dx$, the net lines originating in the box are equal to $(\partial E_x/\partial x)(dx\,dy\,dz)$. Doing the same for the other faces, we obtain the total number of lines originating in the box as

$$\left(\frac{\partial E_x}{\partial x} + \frac{\partial E_y}{\partial y} + \frac{\partial E_z}{\partial z}\right) dx\,dy\,dz = \text{number of lines originating}$$
$$\text{in } dx\,dy\,dz = N$$

By Gauss' law $N = 4\pi q$ where q is the charge contained in the box. Gauss' law then leads to $\partial E_x/\partial x + \partial E_y/\partial y + \partial E_z/\partial z = 4\pi\rho$ when we divide by dx, dy, dz and observe that $\rho = \text{charge/volume} = q/dx\,dy\,dz$. This is the general form of the equation. Since we are considering free space with no charges, Gauss' law states

$$\frac{\partial E_x}{\partial x} + \frac{\partial E_y}{\partial y} + \frac{\partial E_z}{\partial z} = 0 \qquad \text{[M1]}$$

In vector notation*

$$\text{div } \mathbf{E} = 4\pi\rho \qquad \text{with charge density } \rho$$

$$\text{div } \mathbf{E} = 0 \qquad \text{in free space.} \qquad \text{[M1}a]$$

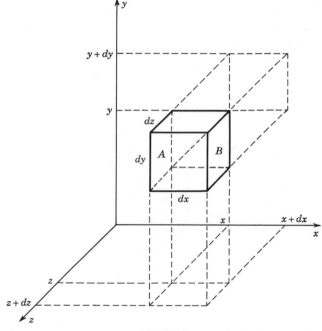

FIGURE 6

Gauss' Law for Magnetic Poles

Since free magnetic poles do not exist, the corresponding quantity to ρ in the magnetic case is always zero. A derivation

* In dielectric materials this equation becomes div $\mathbf{D} = 4\pi\rho$; where $\mathbf{D} = \epsilon\mathbf{E} = \mathbf{E} + 4\pi\mathbf{P}$, ϵ is the dielectric constant, and $\mathbf{P}$ the polarization of the dielectric.

identical to that of 1 will therefore lead to

$$\frac{\partial H_x}{\partial x} + \frac{\partial H_y}{\partial y} + \frac{\partial H_z}{\partial z} = 0 \qquad \text{[M2]}$$

or in vector notation

$$\text{div } \mathbf{H} = 0 \qquad \text{[M2a]}$$

Faraday's Law

To put this law in mathematical form, consider the elementary rectangle as shown in Fig. 7.

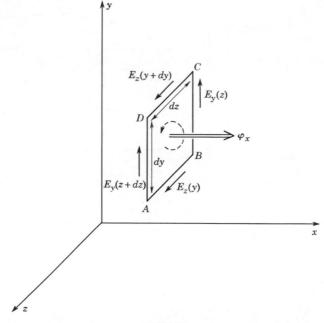

FIGURE 7

The notation $E_z(y)$ means the z component of E at position y, and $E_z(y + dy)$ means the z component of E at position $y + dy$. The dotted circle shows the direction we shall go around the elementary rectangle, and φ shows the flux (which may change) threading through the circuit.

Faraday's law states that the emf around a circuit is

$$\text{emf} = -\frac{1}{c}\frac{d\varphi}{dt} \qquad (7a)$$

We know that emf $= \Sigma \mathbf{E}\cdot\mathbf{dl}$, where $\mathbf{E}$ is the electric field in the direction dl.

Therefore going around our little rectangle $ABCDA$ leads to the following:

$$\frac{\text{Work}}{\text{Charge}} = \text{emf} = \Sigma \mathbf{E}\cdot\mathbf{dl} = -\frac{1}{c}\frac{d\varphi_x}{dt} = -\frac{1}{c}\frac{dB_x}{dt}\,dy\,dz$$
$$= [E_z(y+dy) - E_z(y)]\,dz$$
$$\qquad - [E_y(z+dz) - E_y(z)]\,dy \qquad (7b)$$

Now we know that

$$E_z(y+dy) = E_z(y) + \frac{\partial E_z}{\partial y}\,dy \qquad \text{etc.}$$

Therefore, $\qquad \Sigma \mathbf{E}\cdot\mathbf{dl} = \dfrac{\partial E_z}{\partial y}\,dy\,dz - \dfrac{\partial E_y}{\partial z}\,dz\,dy \qquad (7c)$

So, finally, from $7a$, $7b$, and $7c$,

$$-\frac{1}{c}\frac{\partial B_x}{\partial t} = \frac{\partial E_z}{\partial y} - \frac{\partial E_y}{\partial z} \qquad (7)$$

In free space, $B = H$; and assuming a similar calculation to the above for two mutually perpendicular rectangles, we obtain

$$\frac{\partial E_z}{\partial y} - \frac{\partial E_y}{\partial z} = -\frac{1}{c}\frac{\partial H_x}{\partial t} \qquad [\text{M}3a]$$

$$\frac{\partial E_x}{\partial z} - \frac{\partial E_z}{\partial x} = -\frac{1}{c}\frac{\partial H_y}{\partial t} \qquad [\text{M}3b]$$

$$\frac{\partial E_y}{\partial x} - \frac{\partial E_x}{\partial y} = -\frac{1}{c}\frac{\partial H_z}{\partial t} \qquad [\text{M}3c]$$

In these equations it is useful to note the cyclic interchange of coordinates. In the notation of vector calculus the three equations become one which is written

$$\text{Curl } \mathbf{E} = -\frac{1}{c}\frac{\partial \mathbf{B}}{\partial t} \qquad \text{[M3]}$$

and for free space

$$\text{Curl } \mathbf{E} = -\frac{1}{c}\frac{\partial \mathbf{H}}{\partial t}$$

Ampère's Law of Magnetism

A treatment similar to the above would lead to a relation between the partial space derivatives of H and the current components. We shall not derive this relation because in free space it is not required for we assume the currents to be zero (charge is zero). In the following derivation of the displacement current, it will be clear how the calculation of this section for the case of currents present would proceed.

Displacement Current

The principle role of electric currents in electromagnetism is to produce magnetic fields. Maxwell considered the problem of an interrupted circuit (a wire in series with a condenser) from the standpoint of the magnetic field around it. Consider the circuit of Fig. 8.

The current I is flowing to charge the condenser, but no conduction current is flowing between the plates. The solid circles show the magnetic field produced by the current I. Is there also a magnetic field, as shown dotted, in the region where no conduction current flows? Maxwell assumed that there was, and he attributed this field to a "displacement current" in the condenser. The displacement current may be expressed in terms of dE/dt where E is the field between the condenser plates. It has subsequently been shown that the field shown in heavy dotted line, in Fig. 8, does exist and may be measured. We must therefore admit that the displacement current density (which is really proportional to dE/dt) may produce a magnetic field. This is not unreasonable; since Faraday's law states that changing magnetic fields produce electric fields, one might assume by symmetry that changing electric fields produce magnetic fields. In any event experiment shows that they do.

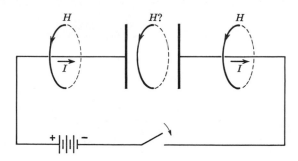

FIGURE 8

We must see how dE/dt and the displacement current are related. Consider the condenser of Fig. 8. The current I flows to charge the condenser. When the condenser has a charge Q, the electric field in the vacuum space is $E = 4\pi Q/A$, where A is the condenser area. Therefore,

$$\frac{dE}{dt} = \frac{4\pi}{A}\frac{dQ}{dt}$$

but

$$\frac{dQ}{dt} = i$$

so,

$$\frac{dE}{dt} = 4\pi\frac{i}{A}$$

It is customary to call the current density $i/A = j$; and, therefore, $j_{esu} = (\tfrac{1}{4}\pi)(dE/dt)$. In this equation both j and E are in esu, i.e., j is (esu charge)/cm^2. If we wished to express j in emu, then the equation would be

$$j_{emu} = \frac{1}{4\pi c}\frac{dE}{dt} \qquad\qquad \text{[M4]}$$

E is, of course, still in esu.

We now proceed to calculate the magnetic field produced by changing electric fields, by using amperes law and acting as if the quantity $(\tfrac{1}{4}\pi c)(dE/dt)$ were a real current of j_{emu}. The derivation is very similar to that for Faraday's law.

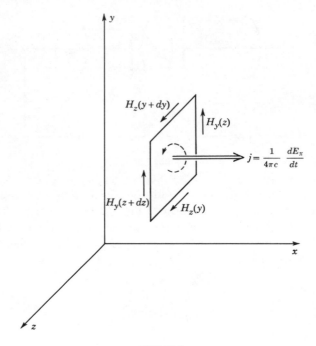

FIGURE 9

Referring to Fig. 9, we see that the application of Ampère's law

$$\Sigma H \cdot dl = 4\pi I \tag{8a}$$

gives

$$\Sigma H \cdot dl = [H_z(y+dy) - H_z(y)]\,dz - [H_y(z+dz) - H_y(z)]\,dy \tag{8b}$$

$$= \left(\frac{\partial H_z}{\partial y} - \frac{\partial H_y}{\partial z}\right)dy\,dz = 4\pi j_x\,dy\,dz \tag{8c}$$

Since
$$j_x = \frac{1}{4\pi c}\frac{\partial E_x}{\partial t}, \qquad (8d)$$

$$\frac{\partial H_z}{\partial y} - \frac{\partial H_y}{\partial z} = \frac{1}{c}\frac{\partial E_x}{\partial t} \qquad [M5a]$$

For similar perpendicular rectangles we get

$$\frac{\partial H_x}{\partial z} - \frac{\partial H_z}{\partial x} = \frac{1}{c}\frac{\partial E_y}{\partial t} \qquad [M5b]$$

and
$$\frac{\partial H_y}{\partial x} - \frac{\partial H_x}{\partial y} = \frac{1}{c}\frac{\partial E_z}{\partial t} \qquad [M5c]$$

We may now summarize the equations for free space.

$$\frac{\partial E_x}{\partial x} + \frac{\partial E_y}{\partial y} + \frac{\partial E_z}{\partial z} = 0 \qquad \text{div } E = 0 \quad [M1]$$

$$\frac{\partial H_x}{\partial x} + \frac{\partial H_y}{\partial y} + \frac{\partial H_z}{\partial z} = 0 \qquad \text{div } H = 0 \quad [M2]$$

$$\left.\begin{aligned} \frac{\partial E_z}{\partial y} - \frac{\partial E_y}{\partial z} &= -\frac{1}{c}\frac{\partial H_x}{\partial t} \qquad &[M3a]\\[1em] \frac{\partial E_x}{\partial z} - \frac{\partial E_z}{\partial x} &= -\frac{1}{c}\frac{\partial H_y}{\partial t} \qquad &[M3b]\\[1em] \frac{\partial E_y}{\partial x} - \frac{\partial E_x}{\partial y} &= -\frac{1}{c}\frac{\partial H_z}{\partial t} \qquad &[M3c] \end{aligned}\right\} \quad \text{Curl } E = -\frac{1}{c}\frac{\partial H}{\partial t}$$

$$\left.\begin{aligned} \frac{\partial H_z}{\partial y} - \frac{\partial H_y}{\partial z} &= \frac{1}{c}\frac{\partial E_x}{\partial t} \qquad &[M5a]\\[1em] \frac{\partial H_x}{\partial z} - \frac{\partial H_z}{\partial x} &= \frac{1}{c}\frac{\partial E_y}{\partial t} \qquad &[M5b]\\[1em] \frac{\partial H_y}{\partial x} - \frac{\partial H_x}{\partial y} &= \frac{1}{c}\frac{\partial E_z}{\partial t} \qquad &[M5c] \end{aligned}\right\} \quad \text{Curl } H = \frac{1}{c}\frac{\partial E}{\partial t}$$

Special Plane-Wave Solution

We shall now show that these equations lead to wavelike solutions. Rather than attempting to solve the equations in their most general form, we will assume a wavelike solution and show that it satisfies the equations. Imagine plane waves travelling in the $+x$ direction. Assume that the vibrations are variations of the **H** and **E** vectors. In the wave front they must be constant over a plane perpendicular to the x axis, i.e., parallel to the yz plane. Therefore, the partial derivatives with respect to y and z must be zero and Maxwell's equations become

$$\frac{\partial E_x}{\partial x} = 0 \qquad\qquad \text{[M1]}$$

$$\frac{\partial H_x}{\partial x} = 0 \qquad\qquad \text{[M2]}$$

$$-\frac{1}{c}\frac{\partial H_x}{\partial t} = 0 \qquad\qquad \text{[M3}a\text{]}$$

$$-\frac{\partial E_z}{\partial x} = -\frac{1}{c}\frac{\partial H_y}{\partial t} \qquad\qquad \text{[M3}b\text{]}$$

$$\frac{\partial E_y}{\partial x} = -\frac{1}{c}\frac{\partial H_z}{\partial t} \qquad\qquad \text{[M3}c\text{]}$$

$$\frac{1}{c}\frac{\partial E_x}{\partial t} = 0 \qquad\qquad \text{[M5}a\text{]}$$

$$-\frac{\partial H_z}{\partial x} = \frac{1}{c}\frac{\partial E_y}{\partial t} \qquad\qquad \text{[M5}b\text{]}$$

$$\frac{\partial H_y}{\partial x} = \frac{1}{c}\frac{\partial E_z}{\partial t} \qquad\qquad \text{[M5}c\text{]}$$

Consider [M5a] and [M1]:

$$\frac{\partial E_x}{\partial x} = 0 \quad\text{and}\quad \frac{1}{c}\frac{\partial E_x}{\partial t} = 0 \quad c < \infty$$

These equations show that E_x is constant in space and time. They represent a superimposed constant field which has nothing to do with the wave. For the wave solution, we may write $E_x = 0$. Similarly Eq. [M3a] and [M2] lead to the conclusion that $H_x = 0$. Since E_x and H_x are zero, the wave is transverse. We now consider the remaining equations in two sets, as illustrated below.

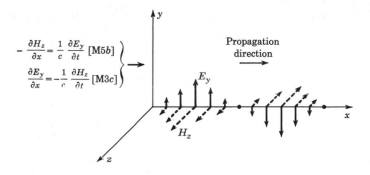

and

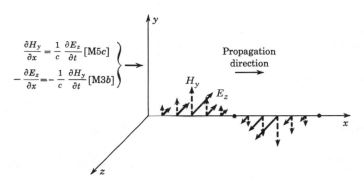

Each set of equations represents a plane polarized wave with E and H perpendicular. These solutions are independent, and any linear combination is also a solution. An equal mixture with 90° phase shift leads to circularly polarized light. We shall use Eq. [M5b] and [M3c] to show that they lead to the wave solution which is sketched beside the equations.

Write the equations

$$\frac{1}{c}\frac{\partial E_y}{\partial t} = -\frac{\partial H_z}{\partial x} \qquad \text{[M5b]}$$

$$c\frac{\partial E_y}{\partial x} = -\frac{\partial H_z}{\partial t} \qquad \text{[M3c]}$$

Differentiate [M5b] with respect to t and [M3c] with respect to x.

$$\frac{1}{c} \frac{\partial^2 E_y}{\partial t^2} = - \frac{\partial^2 H_z}{\partial x \partial t}$$

$$c \frac{\partial^2 E_y}{\partial x^2} = - \frac{\partial^2 H_z}{\partial t \partial x}$$

We see, therefore, that

$$\frac{\partial^2 E_y}{\partial t^2} = c^2 \frac{\partial^2 E_y}{\partial x^2} \qquad \text{[M6a]}$$

Similarly, we can show that

$$\frac{\partial^2 H_z}{\partial t^2} = c^2 \frac{\partial^2 H_z}{\partial x^2} \qquad \text{[M6b]}$$

Equations [M6a] and [M6b] represent the plane wave shown next to Eq. [M5b] and [M3c]. Let us use Eq. [M6a] to show that it satisfies the wave equation. If E_y satisfies the wave equation

$$E_y = f(x - vt) \qquad \text{[M7]}$$

where f is any periodic function of $(x - vt)$, a possible case would be

$$f(x - vt) = A \sin \frac{2\pi}{\lambda} (x - vt) \qquad \text{or} \qquad A \sin k(x - vt)$$

We now differentiate Eq. [M7] and substitute it back into Eq. [M6a].

$$\frac{\partial E_y}{\partial t} = -vf'(x - vt) \qquad \frac{\partial^2 E_y}{\partial t^2} = v^2 f''(x - vt)$$

The ′ and ″ indicate differentiation of f with respect to $(x - vt)$.

$$\frac{\partial E_y}{\partial x} = f'(x - vt) \qquad \frac{\partial^2 E_y}{\partial t^2} = f''(x - vt)$$

Therefore,
$$\frac{\partial^2 E_y}{\partial t^2} = v^2 \frac{\partial^2 E_y}{\partial x^2} \qquad (9a)$$

Comparing with Eq. [M6a], we see that $v = c$, and the *constant c is the free-space velocity of the electromagnetic waves.* This is definitely a new result because one will recall that c previously entered the equations as the ratio of the size of the unit charge in the electrostatic and electromagnetic systems of units, i.e., c esu $=$ 1 emu. This is a remarkable result. Maxwell's theory says that c is a universal velocity of all electromagnetic waves and is also the ratio of the charge units. We can compare this prediction with experiment.

For the ratio of the charges, the measurement of Rosa and Dorsey gives 2.9979×10^{10} cm/sec, and for the velocity of light Michelson's measurement gives 2.99796×10^{10} cm/sec. This remarkable agreement is only one proof of the correctness of Maxwell's formulation.

It is perhaps worth showing that the ratio of charge in the two systems of units must have the dimensions of a velocity.

The definition of q_{esu}* is

$$F_{dynes} = \frac{q^2{}_{esu}}{r^2{}_{cm}}$$

The definition of q_{emu} is

$$F_{dynes} = \frac{(i_{emu}\, ds)^2}{r^2{}_{(cm)}} \qquad i_{emu} = \frac{q_{emu}}{dt}$$

Therefore,

$$q_{(emu)}\, \frac{ds}{dt} = q_{(esu)}$$

The ratio of a charge measured in esu to a charge in emu has the dimensions of a velocity. It follows that if $ds/dt = c$, then c esu of charge $=$ 1 emu of charge. Suppose a charge is equal to 10 statcoulombs.

$$10 \text{ statcoulombs} = 10 \text{ esu } \frac{1 \text{ emu}}{c \text{ esu}} = \frac{10}{3 \times 10^{10}} \text{ emu}$$

This example is given because the conversion of electrical quantities sometimes confuses students although it is like converting any other units, e.g., ft/min to cm/sec. We have been careful to distinguish above between $q_{(emu)}\, c = q_{(esu)}$ (meaning that the charge

---

* Here the subscript q_{esu} means that the charge q is measured in esu.

measured in emu multiplied by c is equal to the charge measured in esu $q_{(esu)}$), and c esu $= 1$ emu (meaning that c electrostatic units of charge are equal to one electromagnetic unit of charge). The smaller the unit of charge the larger is a given charge measured in that unit.

A further example may be useful. We shall consider the forces between charged particles at rest and in motion. Suppose first that two charged particles are at rest. The force between them will be the coulomb attraction or repulsion given by the equation $F = Q_1Q_2/R^2$. In this equation the charges are expressed in esu, and the force is in dynes. Now suppose that one charge is put into motion at constant speed. Will any new force arise? The answer is no. The coulomb force still exists, and the moving charge produces a magnetic field; but no new force arises between the charges. For a new force to arise both charges must be in motion. This new force is the force on a current element in a magnetic field. When both charges are moving at constant speed, one moving charge constitutes a current element which feels a force because of the magnetic field produced by the current element which the other moving charge represents. If both charges are moving with velocity v and have the same sign of charge, the new force will be an attractive force acting in the opposite direction to the coulomb force of repulsion. The magnetic force may be expressed by the equation

$$F = \frac{Q_{1(emu)}Q_{2(emu)}v^2}{R^2} = \frac{Q_1Q_2}{R^2}\frac{v^2}{c^2}$$

The electrostatic and electromagnetic systems of units were introduced in physics because of the different magnitudes of the coulomb and magnetic forces. When the velocity of the particles is small compared to the speed of light, the magnetic force is always $(v/c)^2$ times smaller than the coulomb force.

Returning to our plane-wave solution, we showed that the equation for E_y in the plane wave was

$$\frac{\partial^2 E_y}{\partial t^2} = c^2 \frac{\partial^2 E_y}{\partial x^2}$$

The same procedure applied to H_z leads to the equation

$$\frac{\partial^2 H_z}{\partial t^2} = c^2 \frac{\partial^2 H_z}{\partial x^2} \qquad (9c)$$

These two equations describe the plane polarized wave. They show that both E_y and H_z are propagated with the same universal velocity c. It can be shown that in our units *E and H have equal magnitudes in the electromagnetic wave.* This last result is one of the reasons for using the system of units that we do. Our figures show E and H to be equal, and they are if E is in esu and H in oersted. It should be pointed out that the effect of an electromagnetic wave on a charged particle will come almost entirely through the action of the **E** vector even though E and H are equal. Consider Lorentz's equation

$$\mathbf{F} = e\mathbf{E} + \frac{e}{c}\,\mathbf{v} \times \mathbf{B} \qquad (6)$$

For equal E and B (electromagnetic wave) the ratio R of the electrostatic force to the magnetic force is

$$R = \frac{eE}{\dfrac{e}{c}\,\mathbf{v} \times \mathbf{B}} \qquad B = E \quad \text{and} \quad R = \frac{c}{v}$$

Therefore, the electrostatic forces are larger in the ratio of c/v, and the magnetic forces approach the electric only for particles whose velocities approach the speed of light.

Maxwell's ideas may be extended to show that electromagnetic waves originate when an electric charge is accelerated. This prediction of electromagnetic theory was beautifully verified by the experiments of Heinrich Hertz.

Before temporarily leaving the subject of Maxwell's theory, we must mention the energy and momentum of electromagnetic waves. These concepts are somewhat easier to visualize when we discuss photons, but before the invention of the quantum by Planck and Einstein it was realized that Maxwell's electromagnetic waves carried energy, linear momentum, and — if circularly polarized — angular momentum as well.

We first show that an electromagnetic wave must have energy stored in it by virtue of the existence of its electric and magnetic fields. We consider the case of a plane-parallel vacuum condenser.

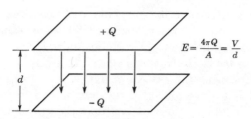

$$E = \frac{4\pi Q}{A} = \frac{V}{d}$$

The work to charge the condenser from $q = 0$ to $q = Q$ or to raise the field from $E = 0$ to $E = E$ is, if V is the potential difference

$$W = \int V\, dq = \int Ed\, dq$$

but since $E = 4\pi q/A$,

$$dq = \frac{A}{4\pi}\, dE$$

and

$$DW = \int^{E} \frac{dA}{4\pi}\, E\, dE$$

or

$$W = \frac{dA}{8\pi}\, E^2$$

Since dA is the volume of space filled with constant field E, we see that

$$\frac{E^2}{8\pi} = \frac{\text{energy}}{\text{volume}} \tag{10a}$$

This is the energy required to create the field, and it is the energy recovered when the field is destroyed. If E is in esu, then $E^2/8\pi = \text{ergs/cm}^3$.

By considering the establishment of a field H in a solenoid, we can show here that the energy stored is

$$\frac{\text{energy}}{\text{volume}} = \frac{H^2}{8\pi} \tag{10b}$$

for a solenoid in a vacuum. If H is in oersteds the energy per unit volume is ergs/cm^3. For dielectric media or media with permeability, the correct expressions for the energy per unit volume are $DE/8\pi$ and $BH/8\pi$. In the free-space electromagnetic wave the energy stored is W where W is the energy/volume.

$$W = \frac{E^2}{8\pi} + \frac{H^2}{8\pi} \qquad (10c)$$

The instantaneous energy density (local)

$$W = \frac{E^2}{4\pi}$$

where $E =$ the local value of the field.

The intensity of an electromagnetic wave is the energy/(area time) crossing a surface. Consider a 1-cm^2 cylinder c cm long. The energy crossing the surface S in one second is Wc. This is the intensity of the wave I.

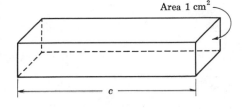

$$I_{\text{inst}} = \frac{E^2}{4\pi} c$$

The last equation for the instantaneous energy flow is a special case of Poynting's theorem which says that the (energy flow)/ (area time) (i.e., intensity) is given by the vector quantity $c/4\pi$ **E** × **H**. This has the numerical value given above, but it also shows the direction of propagation of the wave. Rotation from E to H in the sense of the right-hand screw convention advances in the direction of propagation of energy or of the wave. See the examples below.

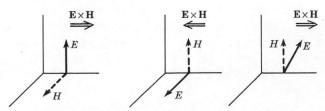

Electromagnetic Waves Carry Momentum

The ratio of the (energy density)/(momentum density) $= c$. We do not prove this result here but will return to it later.

Since

$$I = \frac{\text{energy}}{\text{area time}} = \frac{c}{4\pi} \, \mathbf{E} \times \mathbf{H} = \pi = \text{Poynting's vector} \quad (11a)$$

$$P = \frac{\text{momentum}}{\text{area time}} = \frac{\mathbf{E} \times \mathbf{H}}{4\pi} = \frac{\pi}{c} = \frac{\text{force}}{\text{area}} = \text{radiation pressure}$$
$$\quad (11b)$$

$$p = \frac{\text{momentum}}{\text{volume}} = \frac{\mathbf{E} \times \mathbf{H}}{4\pi c} = \frac{\pi}{c^2} \quad (11c)$$

The above equations show that light carries very little momentum for its energy. Let us consider an example. Sunlight at the earth has an intensity of 2 cal/cm^2 min or 1.4×10^6 ergs/cm^2 sec. Consider 1 cm^2 and 1 sec; 1.4×10^6 ergs are delivered to a black surface. The momentum delivered to the black surface is

$$\frac{1.4 \times 10^6}{3 \times 10^{10}} \cong 5 \times 10^{-5} \text{ dyne-sec}$$

Compare this with a putty ball striking the same surface. The same *kinetic* energy 1.4×10^6 ergs would be delivered by a 100 g putty ball striking at 1.7 m/sec, but the putty ball would deliver 1.7×10^4 dyne-sec of momentum. For the same *kinetic* energy, as the light's total energy, the putty ball delivers 3×10^8 times more momentum. It is easy to show that the ratio of the

$$\frac{\text{Momentum of putty ball}}{\text{Momentum of light}} = \frac{2c}{v}$$

for equality of <u>kinetic</u> energy of putty ball to <u>total</u> energy of light.

We shall see when we consider the *total* energy in relativity, however, that for a given total energy, light carries the most momentum (see Prob. 6). The small momentum per unit energy is strikingly shown in the case of the earth where sunlight brings in 2 hp/m^2 but has so little radiation pressure that its effect is completely negligible with respect to solar gravitation which keeps the earth in its orbit.

As pointed out above, the momentum of light leads to radiation pressure. It can be shown that for light falling normally on a black surface, the radiation pressure is equal to the energy density in the light beam. (Note that energy density and radiation pressure have the same units.) For light falling on a flat reflecting surface the radiation pressure is twice the energy density because the momentum of the light is reversed and, therefore, changes twice as much as in the absorbing case (Probs. 2, 3, 4, and 5).

Light can carry angular momentum as well as linear momentum. Plane polarized light carries no intrinsic angular momentum, circular polarized light carries the maximum. Although the angular momentum of light may be discussed with Maxwell's theory, a more intuitive approach is possible using the concept of photons. We will discuss the quantitative theory in the discussion of photons. It is perhaps worth pointing out that the theory shows that circularly polarized light has a quantity of

$$\frac{\text{angular momentum}}{\text{volume}} = \frac{I}{\omega c},$$

where I is the intensity, and ω is the angular frequency of the light waves. Radio waves are relatively richer in angular momentum than are γ rays.

CHAPTER 2.   Special Relativity

We have now reviewed briefly the concepts of mechanics and electromagnetism required for approaching special relativity. Since the two branches of physics are quite separate, we must see if the Newtonian mechanics and Maxwell's electromagnetism are mutually consistent. The principle of Newtonian relativity is that for all inertial systems the equations of motion have the same form. We proved this on page 4. We can state it mathematically by saying that, if the form of a mechanical equation in Σ is

$$Q(x, y, z, t) = 0$$

then the form will also be

$$Q(x', y', z', t) = 0$$

in Σ' if the transformation is

$$
\begin{array}{lll}
x = x' + vt & \quad \text{or} \quad & x' = x - vt \\
y = y' & & y' = y \\
z = z' & & z' = z
\end{array}
$$

where we have assumed with Newton that $t = t'$. When we try to transform Maxwell's equations with the Galilean transformation, we discover that they are *not invariant*. There is a deep-rooted superstition in physics that *all* physical laws should be invariant under transformation between inertial systems. This, in fact, is one of the Einstein postulates of special relativity. Let us see then how the Galilean transformation fails to transform Maxwell's equations. One way to state Maxwell's results is that a spherical wave is propagated with fixed velocity c in free space. The equation for this in the Σ system would be

$$x^2 + y^2 + z^2 - c^2 t^2 = 0 \qquad (12a)$$

If the equation were invariant, then it would also have to be true that

$$x'^2 + y'^2 + z'^2 - c^2 t^2 = 0 \qquad (12b)$$

but this cannot be. Direct substitution shows that if

$$x^2 + y^2 + z^2 - c^2 t^2 = (x' + vt)^2 + y'^2 + z'^2 - c^2 t^2$$

that

$$x^2 + y^2 + z^2 - c^2 t^2 \neq x'^2 + y'^2 + z'^2 - c^2 t^2$$

unless $v = 0$. More detailed calculations using Maxwell's equations lead to the same conclusion. The difficulty is really that c, according to Maxwell, seems to be a universal constant of nature. What then are the alternatives?

1. The Galilean transformation is correct for mechanics, but Maxwell's equations are not invariant or transform in another way.
2. There is some absolute inertial system in which the velocity of light is c, and it is changed from c in other systems in order that Maxwell's equations may be transformed by the Galilean transformation.
3. There is some other transformation than the Galilean transformation which will make both mechanical and electrodynamical equations transform in an invariant way.

Although other less plausible possibilities have been suggested the three given exhaust the reasonable alternatives. We shall see that alternative (3) was shown to be correct by Einstein but not before extensive experiments had ruled out possibility (2). Alternative (1), although it seriously violates the symmetry of nature, was investigated in some detail by H. Lorentz.

THE MICHELSON-MORLEY EXPERIMENT

If there were a preferred inertial frame, then systems moving with respect to this frame would observe different velocities for light.   The preferred frame was called the *ether frame*.   The "luminiferous ether" was presumed to be the medium propagating electromagnetic waves and to be undetectable in any other way. An unattractive feature of the ether was the following.   It was assumed to be the medium for transmitting *pure* transverse waves.   In order not to transmit any longitudinal waves, it could be shown that the ether had to have essentially infinite rigidity; and yet it is undetectable in a vacuum: Planets move through it without being affected, etc.   Be this as it may, it is speculation and the experiment of Michelson and Morley laid the ether to rest. The earth's velocity in its orbit around the sun is $10^{-4}c$. If the ether is stationary and measurements are made throughout the year, a relative motion of the earth through the ether should be detected.   The Michelson interferometer is sensitive enough to show a relative velocity of $10^{-4}c$. Figure 10 shows the Michelson interferometer.

Light from a source S travels the dotted and solid paths being reflected by the half-silvered mirror M and the front-silvered mirrors M_1 and M_2. This *coherent* light is recombined at P where interference fringes are produced.   It will be shown that if the velocity of light in the direction x is different than that in the direction y, rotation of the interferometer 90° about the axis O will lead to a shift in the fringes observed.   Let us assume that an ether exists.   Let the translational velocity of the earth with respect to the ether be μ. Let c be the velocity of the light ray with respect to the ether and v_e its observed velocity with respect to the terrestrial observer; then,

$$\mathbf{c} = \mathbf{v}_e + \boldsymbol{\mu}$$

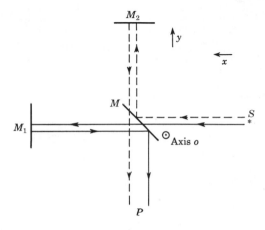

FIGURE 10

Suppose the apparatus is arranged so that the line MM_1 lies along the translational direction through the ether, i.e., along μ, then depending on whether the light is going left or right it will satisfy one of the equations:

$$c = v_1 + \mu$$
$$c = v_1' - \mu$$

v_1 is the velocity observed by the terrestrial observer along MM_1 and v_1' along M_1M. Let v_2 be the velocity with respect to the earth along MM_2, and v_2' that along M_2M. For this second case, v_2 and v_2' are perpendicular to μ so

$$c^2 = v_2{}^2 + \mu^2$$
$$c^2 = v_2'{}^2 + \mu^2$$

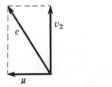

If t_1 is the time required for the light to travel along MM_1 and back and t_2 the time required along MM_2 and back, we have

$$t_1 = \frac{l}{v_1} + \frac{l}{v_1'} = \frac{l}{c - \mu} + \frac{l}{c + \mu} = \frac{2l}{c} \frac{1}{1 - \beta^2} \qquad (13a)$$

and $\quad t_2 = \dfrac{l}{v_2} + \dfrac{l}{v_2'} = \dfrac{2l}{\sqrt{c^2 - \mu^2}} = \dfrac{2l}{c} \dfrac{1}{(1 - \beta^2)^{1/2}}$ (13b)

where $\beta = \mu/c$.

It is easy to show using the binomial theorem that to second order in β

$$t_1 - t_2 = \frac{l}{c}\,\beta^2$$

If λ is the wavelength of light, the time difference $t_1 - t_2$ produces a change in wavelength $\Delta\lambda$ such that

$$\frac{\Delta\lambda}{\lambda} = (t_1 - t_2)f = (t_1 - t_2)\frac{c}{\lambda} = \frac{l}{\lambda}\,\beta^2$$

Since the apparatus is rotated 90°, twice this shift should be observed. The fraction of a fringe width F that the shift should correspond to is

$$F = \frac{2l}{\lambda}\,\beta^2$$

The effective length l is 11 m, the wavelength

$$\lambda = 5.9 \times 10^{-5}\,\text{cm} \qquad \beta = 10^{-4}$$

Therefore, $\quad F = \dfrac{2 \times 10^{-8} \times 11 \times 10^2}{5.9 \times 10^{-5}} = 0.37$

a shift as small as .01 fringes out of the expected .37 could have been detected. *No shift was observed.*

The experiment of Michelson and Morley, therefore, argues strongly against the presence of the ether. The ether, however, had a dying gasp when Fitzgerald and Lorentz suggested that the null result of the Michelson-Morley experiment could be explained if the arm of the interferometer were shortened in its motion through the ether by an amount $1/\sqrt{1 - \beta^2}$. This would make all attempts to observe the ether fail, and it is therefore a very antiphysical assumption (being uncheckable). We shall see that Einstein settled the problem in a much more satisfactory way, but Fitzgerald's contribution is recognized in the relativistic limerick.

There once was a fellow named Fisk
Whose fencing was exceedingly brisk
So swift was his action
The Fitzgerald contraction
Changed the end of his sword to a disk.

We now proceed directly to Einstein's restricted or special theory of relativity. The theory is based on two postulates:

1. All laws of physical phenomena (including mechanical and electrical) are the same for all inertial systems.
2. The velocity of light is a universal constant, the same in all inertial frames.

The statement of the postulates is not exactly that of Einstein but embodies his meaning and fits our previous discussion. The first postulate is really an assumption, the second is a statement of experimental fact (unless we believe the explanation of Fitzgerald for the null result of the Michelson-Morley experiment).

THE LORENTZ TRANSFORMATION

Einstein realized that a single mathematical transformation would satisfy his two postulates. In order to do this, however, one would have to forego Newton's idea of absolute time and consider the time as a variable in the equations, a kind of fourth dimension of space time. Since c is a universal constant, the quantity ct has space dimensions, and in the Einstein theory ct plays a role similar to that of the purely spatial coordinates x, y, z. Since the concept of time is crucial to understanding relativity, we shall have to examine carefully such concepts as the synchronization of clocks; but we shall first present the transformation obtained by Lorentz on purely formal grounds and show that this transformation makes physical laws (and especially those of electromagnetism) invariant under transformation between inertial systems.

As before, we consider system Σ with coordinates x, y, z, t and Σ' with coordinates x', y', z', t'. Σ' moves in the direction of Σ's $+x$ axis with a velocity v. *We assume that at time zero, $t = t' = 0$, the origins of Σ and Σ' coincide, and clocks at the origins of the two* *systems may be compared.* Because of the relative motion, these clocks will never be in coincidence again and may, therefore, never again be directly compared (e.g., by taking a picture of them when they are coincident in space time). We assume, however,

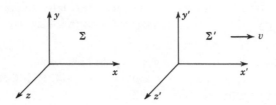

that both systems are equipped with clocks at all points x and x' and that when various clocks come into coincidence they may be compared. We see that synchronizing clocks in a given system is now very important, and we will return to this question. The Lorentz transformation is the following:

$$x = \gamma(x' + \beta ct') \quad [\text{L}_{1a}] \qquad x' = \gamma(x - \beta ct) \quad [\text{L}_{1b}]$$

$$y = y' \quad [\text{L}_{2a}] \qquad y' = y \quad [\text{L}_{2b}]$$

$$z = z' \quad [\text{L}_{3a}] \qquad z' = z \quad [\text{L}_{3b}]$$

$$ct = \gamma(ct' + \beta x') \quad [\text{L}_{4a}] \qquad ct' = \gamma(ct - \beta x) \quad [\text{L}_{4b}]$$

where $\beta = v/c$

$$\gamma = 1/\sqrt{1 - \beta^2}.$$

The equations are written in a form which brings out the similarity of ct and x, y, z and which shows the symmetry of the x and ct transformations. It is also clear that the inverse transformation [L_{1b}], etc., is obtained from [L_{1a}], etc., by simply reversing the primed and unprimed quantities and changing the sign of v (i.e., of β). This is the reciprocal property of the transformation. Sometimes the equality of x and ct is further emphasized by writing the coordinates x, y, z as $x_1 x_2 x_3$ and ct as x_4.

The forward transformation would then be

$$x_1 = \gamma(x'_1 + \beta x'_4)$$
$$x_2 = x'_2$$
$$x_3 = x'_3$$
$$x_4 = \gamma(x'_4 + \beta x'_1)$$

Although the symmetry is somewhat more obvious here, the notation is cumbersome, and we prefer the notation of $[L_{1a}]$, etc. The use of either set, however, is completely a matter of taste.

Invariance of Newton's Laws at Low Speeds

Prior to relativity, mechanical experiments (with the exception of the acceleration of electrons to high energy) were carried out at speeds small compared to c. If $\beta \to 0$, it is easy to see that the Lorentz transformation reduces to the Galilean, and therefore the Galilean transformation must be considered a special case of the Lorentz transformation in which incidentally $t \to t'$. Newton's concept of absolute time is seen to be an approximation valid for transformations in which $\beta \to 0$ or $v \ll c$.

Invariance of Maxwell's Equations

Lorentz obtained the Eqs. $[L_{1a}]$, etc., by asking for invariance of Maxwell's equations in their general form. We shall show a less elegant but simpler example in demonstrating that the Lorentz transformation makes a spherical wave spread uniformly with a velocity c in both coordinate systems. This is not trivial and reflection shows that it is a hard thing to visualize, conditioned as we are to Newtonian thinking. We wish to show that

$$x^2 + y^2 + z^2 - c^2t^2 = x'^2 + y'^2 + z'^2 - c^2t'^2$$

where $c = $ a universal constant.

Substitute the Lorentz transformation in the right-hand side

$$x^2 + y^2 + z^2 - c^2t^2$$
$$= \gamma^2(x' + \beta ct')^2 + y'^2 + z'^2 - \gamma^2(ct' + \beta x')^2$$

Squaring and simplifying the right-hand side leads to

$$y'^2 + z'^2 + \gamma^2(x'^2 - \beta^2 x'^2) + \gamma^2(2\beta x' ct' - 2\beta x' ct') \\ + \gamma^2(\beta^2 c^2 t'^2 - c^2 t'^2)$$

which finally becomes

$$\frac{1}{1 - \beta^2} x'^2(1 - \beta^2) + y'^2 + z'^2 + \frac{c^2 t'^2}{1 - \beta^2}(\beta^2 - 1)$$

or $$x'^2 + y'^2 + z'^2 - c^2 t'^2$$

and, therefore, $$x^2 + y^2 + z^2 - c^2 t^2 = x'^2 + y'^2 + z'^2 - c^2 t'^2$$
$$(14)$$

We should note, however, that this result was not obtained without some cost and additional complication. The Lorentz transformation makes $x = f(x', ct')$ and $ct = f(ct', x')$, i.e., *both x and t are a function of the two variables x' and t', and neither x nor t can be determined without a knowledge of both x' and t'.* We shall proceed to the consequences of this, but first we must discuss the synchronization of clocks according to the Einstein prescription.

SYNCHRONIZATION OF CLOCKS

Because clocks in a given system are usually not at the same place in space, they cannot in general be directly compared. They are usually imagined to be synchronized by the exchange of light signals bearing in mind, of course, that light travels with a velocity c. Let us consider first the analogous situation which might arise in the synchronizing of clocks in a chain of barges using sound as a source. Consider three barges at rest in a river. Barge B in the middle has a whistle and is separated from barges A and C by

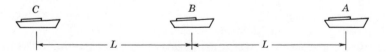

equal distances L. B blows his whistle at the time his clock reads zero. How will A and C synchronize their clocks? They know that sound takes a time $t = L/S$ (where S is the velocity of sound) to travel from B to either A or C. They might adopt the following procedure: Set their clocks ahead to $t = L/S$, and start them at the time of arrival of the sound signal. This could be accomplished with a microphone and a relay. The procedure is illustrated in the diagram where the clock on B starts at zero, and the clocks at

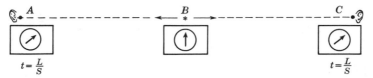

A and C are set at $t = L/S$ and are started on receipt of the sound signal. This is an obvious way to synchronize clocks, and its correctness could be checked by drawing the barges together and comparing the clocks. They would read the same.

However suppose the boats were moving up the river at a speed appreciable with respect to sound. Would the same procedure work? The answer is no. Moving up the river (without a land wind) would produce a relative wind, and if A were the leading boat, it would take a longer time for the signal to reach A and a shorter time to reach C. This is because sound propagates through a medium, and its measured velocity depends on the velocity of the medium. Of course, the boatmen (naturally being physicists) could know this, and A would start his clock at $t_A = L/(S - V)$, and C at $t_C = L/(S + V)$. Again, comparison of the clocks would show the procedure to be correct. In a certain sense, synchronizing clocks with light is even simpler because we need no knowledge of the "ether wind." It does not exist, and light always propagates at velocity c. The procedure outlined for the stationary boats will always work if we simply substitute c, the velocity of light, for S, the velocity of sound. We see, then, that the synchronization of clocks in relativity is just what one would have done by "common sense." To emphasize this, however, we will outline three acceptable ways of synchronizing clocks according to the Einstein prescription.

THREE METHODS OF SETTING CLOCKS

With a Light Flash

The clocks at $-x_0$ and $+x_0$ are set at $+t = x_0/c$. When the clock at the origin reads 0, a light signal (spherical wave) is sent out. When this signal arrives at the clocks at x_0, they are started, but their reading is x_0/c to take account of the propagation of

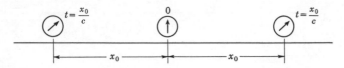

light. We may imagine a master synchronization experiment in which the clocks all along the axis are started as the signal reaches them. This is shown below:

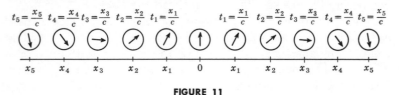

FIGURE 11

We assume the light is propagated through a vacuum, and both phase and group velocities are the same and equal to c.

Slow Transport

Another possibility would be to set all the clocks together at the origin, and then *slowly* carry them to their various positions and set them down. The reason for carrying them slowly will be clear when we discuss general relativity. By slow, we mean $\beta = (v/c) \rightarrow 0$. See Prob. 47.

With Telescopes*

An observer with two telescopes and a split field may observe that clocks are synchronized in the following way: At the point 0,

* A more modern version of this would be to observe the clocks on television screens. The television picture would also show the clock coordinate.

the observer may photograph the origin clock and the images of the clocks at $-x_0$ and x_0. If the clocks are properly synchronized, they will appear as shown with the clocks at $-x_0$ and x_0 reading $-x_0/c$ because of the time required for the light to travel from them. Although this example may seem a little unreal, it is really exactly the same as method 1.

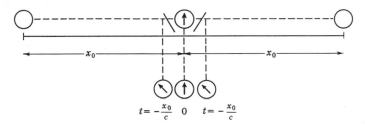

Some thought about the setting of clocks leads one to the belief that any other method would violate Einstein postulate 2, and, in fact, the method adopted is the same as that which can be used in the more pedestrian experiment with sound.

MINKOWSKI DIAGRAMS

We now return to the Lorentz transformation and a graphical representation of it which is due to Minkowski.

The basic property of the Lorentz transformation is that it makes the quantity $x^2 + y^2 + z^2 - c^2t^2$ invariant. This quantity is called the relativistic line element or ground invariant. We shall denote it by G.

$$G = x^2 + y^2 + z^2 - c^2t^2 = x'^2 + y'^2 + z'^2 - c^2t'^2$$

We shall now make a construction which will make G invariant and which displays world points in space time.

This figure should be studied in detail for it shows that for any event in space time symbolized by the world point WP, there is a unique description in each coordinate system, i.e., in Σ the WP is described by $x_1 t_1$ and in Σ' by $x'_1 t'_1$. In spite of the fact that people may be easily confused by relativity, the Minkowski diagram shows that there is always a unique prediction of the theory.

Note that the meaning of the axes is emphasized. The axis of ct means $x = 0$. This line is the world line of the clock at the origin of the Σ system. In a similar way $ct'(x' = 0)$ is the world line of the clock at the origin of the Σ' system. The origin represents the

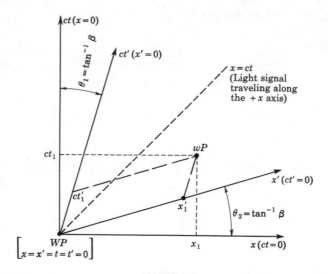

FIGURE 12

coincidence of the clocks at the origin of Σ and Σ' at the time $t = t' = 0 = x = x'$. The angles between the axes are simply computed using the Lorentz transformation. Consider the ct' axis. By definition, $x' = 0$ for this axis. Using [L_{1b}],

$$x' = \gamma(x - \beta ct) = 0$$

and since $\gamma \neq 0$, $x = \beta ct$ is the equation for the ct' axis.

Therefore,
$$\frac{x}{ct} = \tan \theta_1 = \beta$$

as indicated in Fig. 12. Now consider the x' axis for which $ct' = 0$. From [L_{4b}]
$$ct' = \gamma(ct - \beta x) = 0$$

and since $\qquad \gamma \neq 0 \qquad \beta = \dfrac{ct}{x}$

and $\qquad\qquad\qquad \tan \theta_2 = \dfrac{ct}{x} = \beta$

as is shown also in Fig. 12.

One thing remains to make the Minkowski diagram complete. This is the setting of the scales on the axes. Even in the Newtonian case (see Figs. 1 and 2), we had to adjust the scales along the non-coincident t and t' axes.

In what follows it is simpler to use units in which c is 1. This could be done by measuring distances in units of 3×10^{10} cm or times in units of $\frac{1}{3} \times 10^{-10}$ sec. We will see in numerical examples how this works out. Now to set the scales, we must use our fundamental principle that G is invariant. The unit distance on the scales will then be obtained by making $G = \pm 1$. Since we are ignoring y', z', y and z, $G = \pm 1 = x^2 - c^2 t^2 = x'^2 - c^2 t'^2$ is our scale normalizing equation which fixes the *metric* for our construction. We may construct the metric most easily by referring our equations to the lines $x = ct$ and $x = -ct$, which represent the propagation of light signals in the $+x$ and $-x$ directions and which cross the origin at $x = x' = t = t' = 0$.

Consider the ground invariant:

$$x^2 - c^2 t^2 = x'^2 - c^2 t'^2 = G$$

This can be factored:

$$(x + ct)(x - ct) = (x' + ct')(x' - ct') = G$$

Define new axes.

$$x + ct = \eta \quad (\xi = 0) \qquad x' + ct' = \eta' \quad (\xi' = 0)$$
$$x - ct = \xi \quad (n = 0) \qquad x' - ct' = \xi' \quad (\eta' = 0)$$

These axes are shown in Fig. 13. Of course, the η axis is also the η' axis, and the ξ axis is the ξ' axis, because the path of the light signal is unique and represented by one pair of dotted lines at right angles (see Fig. 12). With respect to our new coordinates η, ξ, the metric has a simple form; it is $\eta \xi = \eta' \xi' = G$, or a

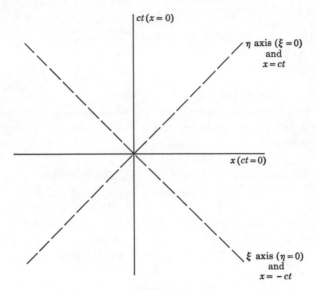

FIGURE 13

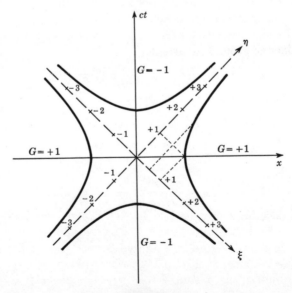

FIGURE 14

simple equilateral hyperbola. If we wish to find unit distance in the metric, we set $G = \pm 1$ and plot $\eta \xi = \eta' \xi' = \pm 1$. This is shown in Fig. 14.

If we wanted to lay out complete scales, we could draw hyperbolas $\eta \xi = \pm 2$, $\xi \eta = \pm 3$, etc.; but we need not, for the scales are linear once the metric is determined. Finally, we superimpose the metric on Fig. 13 to complete the Minkowski diagram.

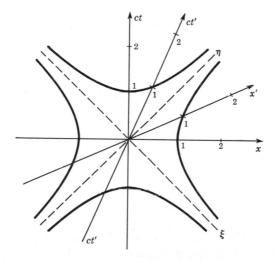

The numbers 1, 2 show the unit measure along the respective scales. We can see now that any world point can be assigned numerical values for x, t, x', and t'. The theory's prediction may always be read off from such a diagram.

There are two remarkable predictions of the special theory which we shall discuss next. They are the time dilatation and the Lorentz contraction.

TIME DILATATION

We shall consider this first from the standpoint of the Lorentz transformation, then illustrate it on a Minkowski diagram. We wish to compare a time interval in the two systems. In one system this time interval between two events may be read on *one and the same clock*. This is the so-called *proper system*, and its clock reads *proper time*. Let us assume that we use the origin clock in Σ' to measure this proper-time interval. In the Σ system the time interval will be the time shown by the clock in coincidence with the origin clock of Σ' at the end of the interval as registered by the clock of Σ'; i.e. at event B. At the beginning of the time interval the origin clocks in Σ and Σ' coincided and both read zero. The physical situation is shown in Fig. 15, where the dotted lines

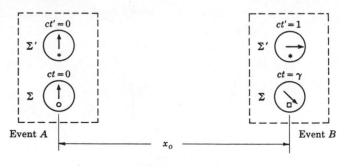

FIGURE 15

encircle coincident clocks which could be photographed and later compared. Objects can be photographed only when they are at the same place. The proper clock is indicated by a *, and the origin clock in Σ by o. The second clock in Σ is indicated by $\square$. The solution is given in the figure, but we will obtain it from the Lorentz transformation. At the beginning of the time interval $x = x' = t = t' = 0$. At the end of the time interval $ct' = 1$ (i.e., one unit of time) and $x' = 0$ for the clock that reads $ct' = 1$. What does the clock in Σ coincident with the origin clock in Σ' read?† Inspection shows that Eq. [L_{4a}] is the appropriate one in this case

$$ct = \gamma(ct' + \beta x')$$

but
$$x' = 0 \quad \text{and} \quad ct' = 1 \tag{15}$$

so
$$ct = \gamma$$

† The reading of this clock is sometimes called "coordinate time."

and the clock in the Σ system shows more elapsed time. *It is always true that the shortest time interval is shown by the proper clock in the proper system.* We can pursue the problem further by asking at what position is the clock in Σ which is compared with the origin clock in Σ' at the end of the time interval? Inspection shows that Eq. [L_{1a}] is the appropriate one in this case.

$$x_0 = \gamma(x' + \beta ct')$$

but $\qquad\qquad x' = 0 \qquad$ and $\qquad ct' = 1$

so $\qquad\qquad x_0 = \gamma\beta \qquad\qquad\qquad\qquad\qquad (15a)$

To take a numerical example, let us assume that the relative velocity of the systems is given by $\beta = 4/5$, then $\gamma = 5/3$. As a result,

$$ct' = 1$$

$$ct = \frac{5}{3}$$

$$x' = 0$$

$$x = \frac{4}{5}\frac{5}{3} = \frac{4}{3}$$

To derive numerical values, $\beta = 4/5$ means Σ' travels at a speed $4/5 \times 3 \times 10^{10} = 2.4 \times 10^{10}$ cm/sec to the right with respect to Σ. When its origin clock reads 1 sec of elapsed time, the clock it coincides with in Σ reads 5/3 sec although the origin clock in Σ

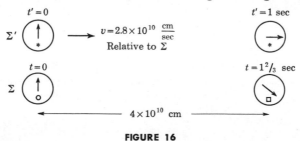

FIGURE 16

read 0 as did the origin clock in Σ' when they passed each other. The position in Σ of the clock that reads 5/3 is $x = 4/3 \times 3 \times 10^{10}$ cm $= 4 \times 10^{10}$ cm from the origin of the Σ system. For concreteness this is shown in Fig. 16.

Finally, we show the solution on a Minkowski diagram. The diagram is drawn for $\beta = 4/5$, $\gamma = 5/3$.

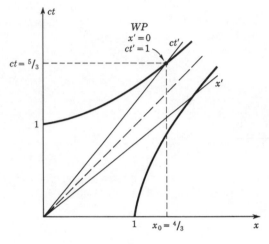

FIGURE 17

In the Minkowski diagram it is clear that the world point represented by the origin clock in Σ' reading $ct' = 1$ is described in the two systems by

$$\begin{array}{ll} x' = 0 & \quad x = \gamma\beta = 4/3 \\ & \text{and} \\ ct' = 1 & \quad ct = \gamma = 5/3 \end{array}$$

Incidentally the clock as observed in the Σ system must be observed to move with velocity βc. That is the requirement of the transformation, and it is satisfied because the velocity is

$$\frac{x}{t} = \frac{\gamma\beta}{\dfrac{\gamma}{c}} = \beta c$$

The time dilatation has been observed for the decay rates of cosmic ray π and μ mesons. We know their proper mean life time from observations on their decay at rest. When they are observed in cosmic rays, they may have velocities approaching the speed of light. For example a γ of 100 is not uncommon. A group of mesons with $\gamma = 100$ is observed to live 100 times longer on the average than the corresponding mesons at rest, in complete agreement with the prediction of relativity.

RELATIVITY AND SIMULTANEITY

In Newton's mechanics, simultaneity had an absolute meaning as did absolute time. In relativity there is no such thing as absolute simultaneity. How could one decide that an event at A was simultaneous with an event at B? The only meaning consistent with relativity would be that the clock at A reads the same as the clock at B, when the clocks and events are, for example, photographed for later comparison: If the photographs indicated by

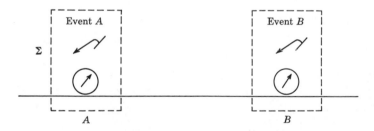

the dotted lines could be compared and the clocks were seen to read the same, the events would be said to be simultaneous in the system Σ. They would, however, *not* in general be simultaneous in any other system in relative motion with respect to Σ. First let us examine the setting of clocks in two systems using the Minkowski diagram. Assume that points A, B, and C are at rest in Σ, and let C lie midway between A and B. At the moment $t = 0$, a light signal is sent out from C in both directions. This is shown in Fig. 18. The arrival of the light signal at A and B is the intersection of the world line of the light ray and the world lines of A and B. It can be seen from Fig. 18 that this happens "simultaneously" at time t_1. In other words an observer in Σ would say that these events are simultaneous. Now suppose an observer

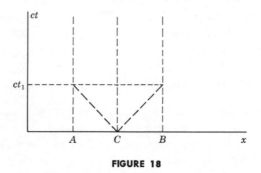

FIGURE 18

in Σ' is synchronizing his clocks (Fig. 19). The world lines are shown at A', C', and B'. Again, a light signal is sent out from

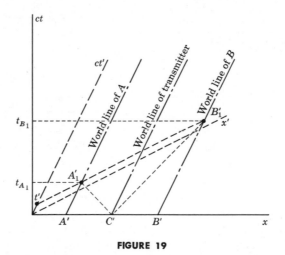

FIGURE 19

C', and its intersection with the world lines of clocks A and B is shown at points A'_1 and B'_1. The events A'_1 and B'_1 are "simultaneous" in Σ' but are manifestly not simultaneous in Σ. They happen at times t_{A_1} and t_{B_1} with event A_1 happening first. We also see from this figure that the x' axis must be inclined with respect to the x axis. In Newtonian diagrams only the ct' axis was inclined. In the Minkowski diagram both are inclined.

Finally, we might ask if it is possible to reverse the time order of events in two systems. *If the events are causally connected, they may not have their order reversed.* If they are not causally connected, even the order of occurrence of the events may be reversed. By causal, we mean that the greatest velocity with which an agency can connect cause and effect is the velocity of light. If event A happens, event B cannot be causally related to it unless a light signal could have propagated from A to B. Let us examine this concept using the Lorentz transformation. Let two events occur simultaneously at x_1 and x_2 in the frame Σ (i.e., $t_1 = t_2$). Then,

$$ct'_1 = \gamma(ct_1 - \beta x_1)$$

$$ct'_2 = \gamma(ct_2 - \beta x_2)$$

and
$$c(t'_2 - t'_1) = \gamma\beta(x_1 - x_2)$$

The events happen at different times in Σ' with $\Delta t' = (t'_2 - t'_1) = \gamma\beta/c \ (x_1 - x_2)$. They may happen in Σ' in either order depending on whether $x_1 > x_2$ or $x_2 > x_1$.

Now let us consider two events happening at different times in Σ. Let us further assume that in Σ event 1 happens first. Therefore, $t_2 - t_1 > 0$ or $t_2 > t_1$. Then we find

$$c(t'_2 - t'_1) = \gamma[c(t_2 - t_1) - \beta(x_2 - x_1)]$$

To obtain a real (not imaginary) time difference in all Σ' systems requires that $v < c$ because $\gamma = 1/(\sqrt{1 - v^2/c^2})$ will be real only for $v < c$. Now $t'_2 - t'_1$ will remain positive as long as $c(t_2 - t_1) > \beta(x_2 - x_1)$ and will certainly be positive if $t_2 - t_1 > (x_2 - x_1)/c$. We see, therefore, that events will happen in the same sequence in all systems if $(x_2 - x_1)/(t_2 - t_1) < c$. This is the definition of causal events; and, therefore, causally connected events cannot have their order reversed. However, the order of events which are not causally connected may be reversed consistent with the equation.

$$t'_2 - t'_1 = \gamma[(t_2 - t_1) - \beta/c(x_2 - x_1)]$$

Because of the causal connection of the events, we see the impossibility of the limerick

> There was a professor named Ney
> Who could travel in a relative way.
> When he left home one night
> At the speed of all light
> He returned on the previous day.

THE LORENTZ CONTRACTION

We now consider the measurement of a length in the system in which a meter stick is at rest (proper length in the proper system) and the observation of this length in a moving coordinate system. Let the proper system be Σ'. The meter stick has length 1(actually a cm stick) in this system. To measure its length in Σ, we must observe both ends at the same time in Σ for example at $t = 0$. The conditions are, therefore, $x' = 1$ and $t = 0$. Examination shows that the appropriate equation is [L_{1b}]:

$$x' = \gamma(x - \beta ct) \qquad [L_{1b}]$$

Substituting $x' = 1$ and $t = 0$ gives

$$x' = 1 = \gamma x \qquad (16)$$

Since x is the length measured in Σ, *the moving system measures the length shorter in the ratio of* $1/\gamma$. This could also be expressed in the following way. The proper length is the length measured in the system in which the meter stick is at rest. This length will appear shorter in the ratio of γ to observers in any coordinate frame in relative motion with respect to the proper frame. *The shortening of moving meter sticks is called the Lorentz contraction and the slowing down of moving clocks is called the time dilatation.* The solution for the Lorentz contraction is shown in Fig. 20.

The axis ct' and the dashed line b^0b' are the world lines of the two ends of the meter stick. The observer in Σ must measure the stick at $t = 0$; i.e., when each end coincides with the x axis (for which $t = 0$). In the Σ' system the length is given by the line $a'b'$. The metric heavy line is arranged to make this length 1. The observer in Σ sees the length as $a'b^0$.

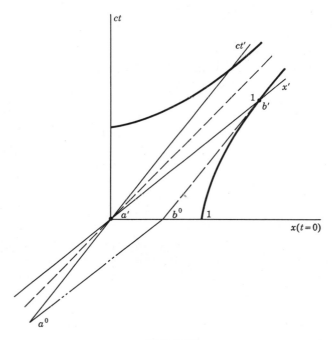

FIGURE 20

The unit of length in his system is shown by the heavy-lined metric. The length $a'b^0$ is shorter than this, and geometry shows that $a'b^0 = 1/\gamma$ as we found from the Lorentz transformation. This Lorentz contraction is to be distinguished from that suggested by Fitzgerald and Lorentz to explain the null result of the Michelson-Morley experiment. In that case they suggested a real contraction of the meter stick in the system in which it is at rest. The actual contraction is that of a length as measured by a moving observer. Without both the time dilatation and the Lorentz contraction, relativity would be inconsistent. Let us consider an example. Mesons have lifetimes given by the following radioactive equation:

$$\frac{dN}{dt} = -\frac{N}{\tau_0} \quad \text{or} \quad N = N_0 e^{-t/\tau_0}$$

τ_0 is the mean lifetime. Observations on many decays allow τ_0 to be determined with high precision. For the sake of simplicity let us consider, then, one particle which lives at rest a lifetime τ_0 (proper lifetime). Suppose this is a cosmic ray meson which enters the atmosphere with $\beta \to 1$ and $\gamma > 1$. We must describe its decay in its own system which we will call Σ' and in the earth system which we will call Σ. As observed from Σ, the meson travels a distance L (measured in Σ) before it decays (dies).

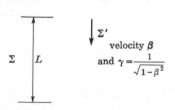

In the Σ system the meson has its lifetime dilated to $\gamma\tau_0$; therefore, the distance it travels before decay is given by $L = \gamma\tau_0 c$ (we approximate its velocity by c because $\beta \to 1$).

In the Σ' system the meson lives only τ_0, but the length L as observed in Σ' is Lorentz contracted L/γ. In this system the meson decays when $L/\gamma = c\tau_0$, or we see that $L = \gamma\tau_0 c$, the same result inferred from the Σ system. Both observers, therefore, consistently describe the event and could predict the same answer. A nonrelativistic observer, however, would have predicted $L = \tau_0 c$. This would be grossly in error. Consider a meson with a mean life of 2×10^{-8} sec (π meson). Suppose the meson has $\gamma = 100$. The value of β will be $\gamma = 1/\sqrt{1 - \beta^2} = 100$ or $\beta = .99995$. The distance traveled before decay measured in the Σ system is

$$L = \underset{\gamma}{100}(\underset{c}{3 \times 10^{10}})(\underset{\tau_0}{2 \times 10^{-8}})$$

or $$L = 6 \times 10^4 \text{ cm} = 600 \text{ m}$$

The nonrelativistic observer would have predicted a distance of only 6 m. *The relativistic value is confirmed by experiment!*

A misconception about the effect of the Lorentz contraction has been propagated for the 55 years that special relativity has been known. It has to do with the apparent shape of rapidly moving objects and has only recently been correctly treated by J. Terrell (1959). What was commonly said was that the Lorentz contraction would make a moving sphere become an ellipsoid as viewed by an observer in another system and would foreshorten the size of a cube. Terrell has shown that this is not correct: a sphere still looks like a sphere, and a cube has no apparent foreshortening; but the effect of the transformation is only to make the object appear to be rotated. The argument is so straightforward that we reproduce it here for the case of a cube. The simplicity and elegance of Terrell's treatment is proof that even with the close scrutiny that special relativity has had, fundamental points can still be discovered about it.

The feature of the problem which was previously overlooked was that light leaves different parts of the moving object at different times. To photograph the object, the light must reach the observer at the same time. (Imagine an infinitely fast camera shutter.) We will first consider a "nonrelativistic" case. We assume that light propagates with velocity c

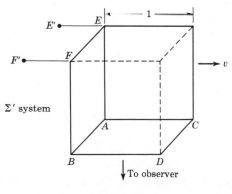

FIGURE 21

in the observer's frame. Consider a cube with each side 1 cm in length. It is moving as indicated. The cube is shown in perspective so that the edges may be identified (see Fig. 21).

The side $ABCD$ is equidistant from the observer; it will, therefore, appear undistorted. However, light leaving E and F must leave earlier to arrive at the observer at the same time as light from $ABCD$. Therefore, this light would be emitted when the points EF were at $E'F'$. The observer sees some of the back of the cube. Figure 22a shows the result.

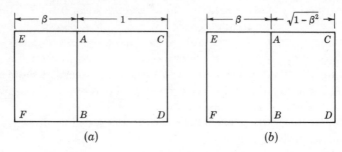

(a)   (b)

FIGURE 22

Now consider a relativistic observer. Because sides BF and AE are perpendicular to the motion, he sees the same $ABFE$ as the nonrelativistic observer. However, the sides BD and AC are Lorentz contracted by the factor $\sqrt{1 - \beta^2}$. They are, therefore, seen shorter. He sees the cube as Fig. 22b. Figure 22 is drawn for $\beta^2 = .5$. Examination of this figure shows that the nonrelativistic observer sees a distorted cube, but the relativistic observer sees an undistorted cube rotated through an angle $\sin^{-1}\beta$. In our figure he sees the cube rotated through 45°. The Lorentz contraction exists but is just the right size to make the figure rotate without distorting. This result has been shown to hold for objects of all shapes, provided the object subtends a small solid angle at the observer. We see that, in this case, relativity fits ones intuition that things should "look the same," and the nonrelativistic model gives a distorted picture.*

* For a more complete treatment of this problem and for several interesting examples see V. F. Weisskopf, "The Visual Appearance of Rapidly Moving Objects," *Physics Today*, XIII, No. 9 (September, 1960).

DYNAMICAL QUANTITIES

We must now consider the meaning of various dynamical quantities in relativity. For example: How shall we formulate the conservation laws? How will velocities add? Most important: What dynamical quantities, if any, are invariant under Lorentz transformations? It is worth pointing out that we must always be on the alert to see that the relativistic prediction reduces to the Newtonian one when $v < c$ or $\beta \to 0$ or $\gamma \to 1$.

THE COMPOSITION OF VELOCITIES

We may derive the velocity addition law formally by applying the Lorentz transformation to quantities like

$$v_x = \frac{dx}{dt} \quad \text{and} \quad v'_x = \frac{dx'}{dt'} \quad \text{etc.}$$

The definitions of velocities are

$$v_x = \frac{dx}{dt} \qquad v'_x = \frac{dx'}{dt'}$$

$$v_y = \frac{dy}{dt} \qquad v'_y = \frac{dy'}{dt'}$$

$$v_z = \frac{dz}{dt} \qquad v'_z = \frac{dz'}{dt'}$$

From Eq. *L1b, 2b, 3b, 4b:*

$$dx' = \gamma(dx - \beta c\, dt) \qquad dy' = dy$$
$$c\, dt' = \gamma(c\, dt - \beta\, dx) \qquad dz' = dz$$

and $$\frac{dx'}{c\, dt'} = \frac{\gamma(dx - \beta c\, dt)}{\gamma(c\, dt - \beta\, dx)} = \frac{\dfrac{dx}{dt} - \beta c}{c - \beta \dfrac{dx}{dt}}$$

Therefore $$\frac{1}{c} v'_x = \frac{v_x - v}{c - (v/c)v_x} \quad \text{and} \quad v'_x = \frac{v_x - v}{1 - vv_x/c^2}$$

Similarly, we can find v'_y and v'_z.

The complete transformation is finally

$$v'_x = \frac{v_x - v}{1 - vv_x/c^2} \tag{17a}$$

$$v'_y = \frac{v_y}{\gamma(1 - vv_x/c^2)} \tag{17b}$$

$$v'_z = \frac{v_z}{\gamma(1 - vv_x/c^2)} \tag{17c}$$

$$v_x = \frac{v'_x + v}{1 + vv'_x/c^2} \tag{17d}$$

$$v_y = \frac{v'_y}{\gamma(1 + vv'_x/c^2)} \tag{17e}$$

$$v_z = \frac{v'_z}{\gamma(1 + vv'_x/c^2)} \tag{17f}$$

We have written the inverse transformation without specific calculation by exchanging the primed and unprimed quantities and by reversing the sign of v wherever it occurs. This is often a labor-saving device.

We note in these equations that if $v/c \to 0$, the equations reduce to the Galilean transformation; e.g., if $\beta \to 0$, $v'_x = v_x - v$. In a problem we ask the student to show that the transformation always makes the speed of light in a vacuum equal to c, i.e., $\mu'^2 = v'^2_x + v'^2_y + v'^2_z$. If $\mu = c$, it will follow that $\mu' = c$. We use the symbol μ for the velocity to avoid confusion with v which is the relative velocity of the two systems. Consider the following specific case:

Two electrons are traveling at $v = .9c$ in opposite directions as observed from a system Σ. What is the velocity of one electron

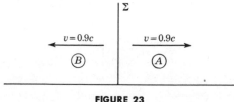

FIGURE 23

with respect to the other? Transform to a system Σ' traveling to the right with velocity $.9c$. This moves with electron A.

We see that

$$v = .9c$$

$$v_x = -.9c$$

Therefore $v'_x = \dfrac{v_x - v}{1 - (v_x v/c^2)} = \dfrac{-.9c - .9c}{1 + (.81c^2/c^2)} = -\dfrac{1.8}{1.81} c$

So relative to electron A, electron B travels in the $-x'$ direction with speed $1.8/1.81c$.

The Velocity c Cannot Be Exceeded

If the previous example had taken "photons" of velocity c instead of electrons at $0.9c$, the result for v'_x would have been

$$v'_x = -c$$

Even though photons have velocities $+c$ and $-c$ in the Σ system, the photons travel with velocity c with respect to each other. This, of course, is necessary to satisfy Einstein postulate 2, which represents the result of experiment and the prediction of Maxwell's equations. One may ask whether there are not differences between the photons observed in Σ and the photon A observed from the system of photon B. The answer is yes, and we shall see what these differences are when we study the optical Doppler effect.

THE CONSERVATION OF MOMENTUM AND MASS OF A MOVING OBJECT

The conservation of momentum is the most inviolate principle in physics. We, therefore, construct relativity to conserve it.

Let us consider a simple experiment to see the consequences of the Lorentz velocity transformation plus the conservation of momentum. The example is the inelastic collision of two balls of equal mass in Σ'. They roll together with velocities μ' and $-\mu'$ in this system and stick together. We shall describe the collision in Σ and in Σ'.

The conservation of momentum is

$$m'\mu' - m'\mu' = 0 \qquad \text{in } \Sigma'$$

$$m_1\mu_1 + m_2\mu_2 = (m_1 + m_2)v \qquad \text{in } \Sigma$$

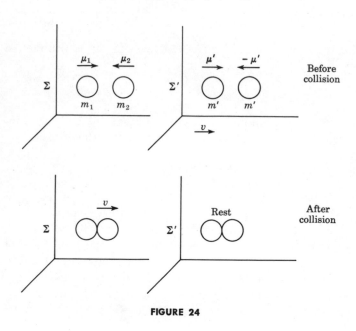

FIGURE 24

The velocities μ_1 and μ_2 in Σ are

$$\mu_1 = \frac{\mu' + v}{1 + (\mu'v/c^2)} \qquad \text{and} \qquad \mu_2 = \frac{-\mu' + v}{1 - (\mu'v/c^2)}$$

Simultaneous solution of the equations leads to

$$\frac{m_1}{m_2} = \frac{1 + (\mu'v/c^2)}{1 - (\mu'v/c^2)} = \frac{\sqrt{1 - \mu_2{}^2/c^2}}{\sqrt{1 - \mu_1{}^2/c^2}}$$

and, therefore,

$$m_1\sqrt{1 - \mu_1{}^2/c^2} = m_2\sqrt{1 - \mu_2{}^2/c^2} = m_0$$

When the ball is at rest its mass is m_0. The mass in motion must, therefore, be

$$m = \frac{m_0}{\sqrt{1 - v^2/c^2}}$$

where v is understood to be the velocity of the mass with respect to the observer We may, therefore, write

$$m = \frac{m_0}{\sqrt{1 - \beta^2}} = \gamma m_0$$

The result is that an object observed at high speed has a larger mass than when at rest. If $\beta \to 0$, $m \to m_0$, the rest mass. If $\beta \to 1$, $m \to \infty$. This shows that to make a material particle travel at the speed of light would require raising its mass to infinity. This is another indication that c is a limiting velocity. The above predictions can be accurately verified by accelerating electrons to high energy and measuring their momentum by bending them in a magnetic field. The result of the experiment shows that either the mass increases according to $m = m_0/\sqrt{1 - \beta^2}$ or the charge e on the electron decreases in the same ratio. We have reason to believe that the charge is a fundamental invariant and, therefore, take the electron experiment to demonstrate the relativistic increase in mass. Incidentally, the atom gives one of the best examples that the charge is not affected by the speed. In heavy atoms, the inner electrons travel at velocities comparable with c. If the charge decreased with increasing speed, these atoms would be positively charged. They are observed to be neutral to a very high order of accuracy. We, therefore, know it is *mass* which changes with velocity as predicted by relativity. We shall take numerical examples in the electron case after developing several other concepts.

Work and Kinetic Energy

We have seen that momentum in the sense of

$$mv = \frac{m_0}{\sqrt{1 - \beta^2}} v = m_0 \gamma \beta c$$

is conserved in special relativity. We must now examine our other mechanical concepts. What do we mean by kinetic energy? In classical mechanics the kinetic energy $T = \int F\,ds$, and we know that since the mass changes, we must use for $F = d(mv)/dt$. We now employ a procedure which may not be rigorously justified. We assume that we may calculate $T = \int \dfrac{d(mv)}{dt}\,ds$. This means (since v is changing) that we are going from one inertial system to another whereas special relativity so far has applied only to the relations between inertial systems. The *assumption* that we may find T by calculating $\int F\,ds$ leads to interesting conclusions which again may be checked by experiment. We, therefore, proceed with the calculation

$$T = \int F\,ds = \int \frac{d(mv)}{dt}\,ds = \int \frac{ds}{dt}\,d(mv) = \int v\,d(mv)$$

We could substitute for

$$m = \frac{m_0}{\sqrt{1 - v^2/c^2}}$$

and carry out the calculation. Doing this leads to mathematical complications. We, therefore, make a trigonometric substitution which we shall find useful in solving many problems. Introduce a variable Θ such that $\sin\Theta = \beta$. Then, since

$$\gamma = \frac{1}{\sqrt{1 - \beta^2}} = \frac{1}{\sqrt{1 - \sin^2\Theta}} = \frac{1}{\cos\Theta} = \sec\Theta$$

We see, then, that

$$v = c\sin\Theta$$
$$mv = m_0 c \tan\Theta$$
$$d(mv) = m_0 c \sec^2\Theta\,d\Theta$$

and T becomes

$$T = \int_0^\Theta m_0 c^2 \sin\Theta \sec^2\Theta\,d\Theta$$

This easily integrates to

$$T = m_0 c^2 \left[\frac{1}{\cos\Theta}\right]_0^\Theta$$

where Θ represents the final value of θ for the value of v acquired after the force has done its work. The solution is then

$$T = m_0 c^2 (\sec \Theta - 1) = m_0 c^2 (\gamma - 1)$$

Let us write this expression out

$$T = m_0 c^2 \left(\frac{1}{\sqrt{1 - \beta^2}} - 1 \right)$$

If $v \to 0$, we see that $T \to 0$, as it does nonrelativistically. We can also show by expansion with the binomial theorem that

$$T = \frac{1}{2} m_0 v^2 + \frac{3}{8} m_0 v^2 \frac{v^2}{c^2} + \cdots$$

If $v < 1$, this series is well-approximated by

$$T = \frac{1}{2} m_0 v^2$$

the classical expression for the kinetic energy. We, therefore, take as the definition of kinetic energy in relativity

$$\boxed{T = m_0 c^2 (\sec \Theta - 1) = m_0 c^2 (\gamma - 1) = m_0 c^2 \left(\frac{1}{\sqrt{1 - \beta^2}} - 1 \right)}$$

If we further remember that

$$mc^2 = \frac{m_0 c^2}{\sqrt{1 - \beta^2}}$$

$$\boxed{T = (m - m_0) c^2} \qquad (18a)$$

This shows that the increase in kinetic energy comes about because of the increase in mass or

$$\Delta T = \Delta m c^2$$

This makes it attractive to assume that all mass has energy associated with it and that the total energy ε is the sum of the rest energy and the kinetic energy

$$\mathcal{E} = T + m_0 c^2$$

and, therefore, $\mathcal{E} = mc^2 - m_0 c^2 + m_0 c^2$

or

$$\boxed{\mathcal{E} = mc^2} \tag{18b}$$

If m is given in grams and c in cm/sec, $\mathcal{E}$ will be expressed in ergs. One gram of matter is, therefore, equivalent to 9×10^{20} ergs. *The theory of relativity ascribes mass to all energy and energy to all mass.* If we take the sun as an example of mass energy, we can calculate that in each second the sun radiates 10^{26} calories or about 4×10^{33} ergs. It, therefore, radiates 4.4×10^{12} g of energy/sec

$$\frac{4 \times 10^{33} \text{ ergs}}{9 \times 10^{20} \text{ ergs/g}}$$

Its mass decreases by the mass of the radiated energy or by 4.4×10^{12} g/sec. We know that the sun burns hydrogen to helium to produce its energy, and in this process approximately 6×10^{-3} of the mass is converted into energy. The mass of the sun is 2×10^{33} g of which about half is hydrogen or about 10^{33} g. There is, thus, available $6 \times 10^{-3} \times 10^{33} = 6 \times 10^{30}$ g energy. At the present rate of 4.4×10^{12} g/sec, the sun could be expected to live

$$\frac{6 \times 10^{30}}{4.4 \times 10^{12}} = 1.35 \times 10^{18} \text{ sec}$$

There are $\pi \times 10^7$ sec in a year; therefore, the sun should not burn out for 4×10^{10} years; no need to worry about our supply of heat for some time!

The relation we have given

$$\mathcal{E} = T + m_0 c^2$$

is for a free particle not in a potential field. Potential energy also has mass. A compressed spring weighs more than one which is slack, by virtue of the potential energy of compression. A calculation, however, will convince one that the fractional change in mass of a compressed spring is indeed small.

THE RELATION BETWEEN ENERGY AND MOMENTUM

There is useful relation between total energy and momentum. This is

$$\mathcal{E}^2 = p^2c^2 + m_0{}^2c^4$$ momentum $mv = p$

We can easily prove this by using our trigonometric substitution $\beta = \sin \Theta$

$$\mathcal{E}^2 = m_0{}^2c^4 \sec^2 \Theta \qquad p^2c^2 = m_0{}^2c^4 \tan^2 \Theta$$

and $\quad m_0{}^2c^4 \sec^2 \Theta = m_0{}^2c^4 \tan^2 \Theta + m_0{}^2c^4 \qquad Q.E.D.$

Another form of this equation which is sometimes useful is obtained by observing that

$$\mathcal{E}^2 = (T + m_0c^2)^2$$

so that $\qquad (T + m_0c^2)^2 = p^2c^2 + m_0{}^2c^4$

which leads to

$$T^2 + 2Tm_0c^2 = p^2c^2 \tag{18c}$$

These equations are sometimes written in the normalized form.

$$\left(\frac{\mathcal{E}}{m_0c^2}\right)^2 = \left(\frac{p}{m_0c}\right)^2 + 1 \tag{18d}$$

If $\mathcal{E}$ is expressed in units of m_0c^2, T in units of m_0c^2, and p in units of m_0c, then all problems are identical. The square root of the equation

$$\mathcal{E}^2 = p^2c^2 + m_0{}^2c^4$$

is called the Dirac equation in quantum mechanics.

It should be pointed out that m_0c^2 is an invariant in relativity. This means that $\mathcal{E}^2 - p^2c^2$ is also an invariant. The three components of pc and $\mathcal{E}$ transform as do the three space coordinates and ct. Such transforming quantities are called 4 vectors because they are invariant in four-dimensional space as ordinary vectors are in three-dimensional space. The relations between T, $\mathcal{E}$, p and $m_0 c^2$ can be conveniently shown in a simple right triangle which is really based on our trigonometric transformation. We

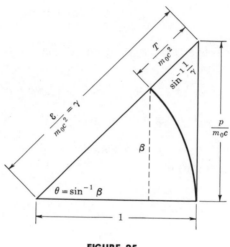

FIGURE 25

show it in normalized units. Substitution in the previously derived equations will verify that the above figure does represent them.

THE LORENTZ FORCE AND RELATIVITY

In Eq. 6 we wrote the Lorentz force

$$\mathbf{F} = e\mathbf{E} + \frac{e}{c}\,\mathbf{v} \times \mathbf{B} \tag{6}$$

We consider it term by term. The first term is the electrostatic force. It is equivalent to saying that the kinetic energy gained by a particle in falling through a potential difference V is $T = Ve$. Nonrelativistically, this would mean that $\frac{1}{2}mv^2 = Ve$. If we apply this equation to an electron falling through a potential of 2×10^6 volts, what do we get?

$$Ve = 2 \times 10^6 \text{ electron volts}$$

$$m_0 c^2 \text{ for an electron } = \frac{9 \times 10^{-28} \times 9 \times 10^{20}}{1.6 \times 10^{-12}}$$

or $m_0 c^2 = .51 \times 10^6 \text{ ev}$ or $.51 \text{ Mev}$

$$\frac{1}{2} m_0 v^2 = \frac{1}{2} m_0 \beta^2 c^2 = Ve$$

or $\beta^2 = \dfrac{2Ve}{m_0 c^2} = \dfrac{(2)2 \times 10^6}{.51 \times 10^6}$

This would give $\beta^2 = 8$ or $\beta = 2.4$

The nonrelativistic calculation would have the 2-Mev electron going at nearly three times the speed of light. This is impossible, and comes from substitution of the wrong value for T. We should have used $T = m_0 c^2 (\gamma - 1)$. Let us try again.

$$T = m_0 c^2 (\gamma - 1) = 2 \times 10^6 \text{ ev}$$

$$m_0 c^2 = .51 \times 10^6$$

So $\gamma - 1 = \dfrac{2 \times 10^6}{.51 \times 10^6} \cong 4$

$$\gamma = 5 = \frac{1}{\sqrt{1 - \beta^2}}$$

Therefore, $1 - \beta^2 = \dfrac{1}{25}$

Further, $\beta^2 = 1 - .04$, and $\beta = 1 - .02 = .98$. We see that the relativistic expression gives a velocity less than that of light. Incidentally, the mass of our electron is given by $\gamma = mc^2/m_0 c^2 = 5$; therefore, the electron with kinetic energy of 2 Mev has a mass five times as great as its rest mass. Four units of mc^2 come from the kinetic energy and one unit from the rest mass energy. Here is a case where the kinetic energy weighs four times as much as the rest energy.

We now consider the second part of the Lorentz force.

$$\mathbf{F}_{\text{mag}} = \frac{e}{c}\,\mathbf{v} \times \mathbf{B}$$

Again, we would get in trouble if we assumed that

$$F_{\text{mag}} = \frac{m_0 v^2}{R}$$

as we would do nonrelativistically. The expression that is correct, however, is

$$F_{\text{mag}} = \frac{m v^2}{R}$$

and the Lorentz force then leads to the equation (for v and $B \perp$ to one another)

$$\frac{m v^2}{R} = \frac{e}{c}\,vB \qquad \text{or} \qquad mv = \frac{e}{c}\,BR$$

mv is the relativistic momentum p.

We see that
$$\boxed{\frac{p}{e} = \frac{BR}{c}} \tag{19}$$

For a singly charged particle, it follows that

$$p = \frac{e}{c}\,BR = \frac{4.8 \times 10^{-10}}{1.6 \times 10^{-12}}\,BR\,\frac{\text{ev}}{c}$$

where ev = electron volts.

Therefore,
$$\boxed{p = 300\,BR\,\frac{\text{ev}}{c}} \tag{19a}$$

The unit ev/c for momentum is commonly used because energies then come out in ev. The quantity BR is called the *magnetic rigidity*. It is determined by the momentum per unit charge

$$\left(\frac{p}{q}\right) = 300\,BR\,\frac{\text{ev}}{c}$$

where q is expressed in unit charges; (i.e., for a singly charged particle $q = 1$, for a doubly charged particle $q = 2$, etc.)

We now apply some of the previous ideas to a numerical example. A singly charged particle describes an arc of 50-cm radius in a

What is its:	Momentum	Kinetic energy	$\dfrac{1}{\beta^2}$
If it is:			
An electron	?	?	?
A 200-mass meson	?	?	?
A proton	?	?	?

uniform magnetic field of 10,000 gauss. We wish to fill in the above table. The reason we calculate $1/\beta^2$ is that we shall see in the study of energy loss of charged particles that the ionization of singly charged particles (by which they are observed) is $I \approx 1/\beta^2$. For all the particles in our example the momentum is the same, because the radius of curvature and the magnetic field are fixed

$$p = 300\, BR = 300(10{,}000)50 = 150\ \frac{\text{Mev}}{c}$$

1. Electron:

$$m_0 c^2 = .51\ \text{Mev}$$
$$\mathcal{E}^2 = p^2 c^2 + m_0{}^2 c^4$$
$$= (150)^2 + (.51)^2$$

We can neglect the $(.51)^2$, and $\mathcal{E} = 150$ Mev. Therefore, the kinetic energy

$$T = \mathcal{E} - m_0 c^2 = \underline{149.5\ \text{Mev}}$$

2. A 200-mass meson:

$$m_0 c^2 = (.51)(200) = 102\ \text{Mev}$$
$$\mathcal{E}^2 = (150)^2 + (102)^2$$
$$= 2.25 \times 10^4 + 1.04 \times 10^4 = 3.29 \times 10^4$$
$$\mathcal{E} = 181\ \text{Mev}$$
$$T = \mathcal{E} - m_0 c^2 = 181 - 102 = \underline{79\ \text{Mev}}$$

3. Proton:

$$m_0 c^2 = 931 \text{ Mev}$$
$$\mathcal{E}^2 = (150)^2 + (931)^2$$
$$= 2.25 \times 10^4 + 86.5 \times 10^4 = 88.8 \times 10^4$$
$$\mathcal{E} = 942 \text{ Mev}$$
$$T = \mathcal{E} - m_0 c^2 = 942 - 931 = \underline{11 \text{ Mev}}$$

In the above cases the electron is extremely relativistic, the meson is intermediate, and the proton is nonrelativistic. We can see this by calculating γ and β.

Calculation of γ and β and $1/\beta^2$

1. Electron

$$\gamma = \frac{\mathcal{E}}{m_0 c^2} = \frac{150}{.51} \cong 300$$

$$= \frac{1}{\sqrt{1 - \beta^2}} \quad \text{and} \quad 1 - \beta^2 = \left(\frac{1}{300}\right)^2$$

So
$$\beta^2 = 1 - \left(\frac{1}{300}\right)^2$$

and
$$\beta = 1 - \frac{1}{2}\left[\frac{1}{9 \times 10^4}\right] = 1 - \frac{1}{1.8 \times 10^5}$$

so
$$\beta = .9999945$$

and
$$\frac{1}{\beta^2} = 1.00001$$

Note that β and $1/\beta^2$ can be calculated to high accuracy without the use of log tables but using the binomial expansion.

2. Meson

$$\gamma = \frac{181}{102} = 1.775$$

$$\sqrt{1 - \beta^2} = \frac{1}{\gamma} = .563 \quad \text{and} \quad 1 - \beta^2 = .317$$

So $\qquad \beta^2 = .683 \qquad \dfrac{1}{\beta^2} = 1.41 \qquad \beta = .826$

3. Proton

An 11-Mev proton is nonrelativistic

So, $\qquad \dfrac{1}{2} m_0 c^2 \beta^2 = 11 \qquad$ and $\qquad \dfrac{1}{2} \beta^2 = \dfrac{11}{931}$

$$\beta^2 = \dfrac{22}{931} \qquad \dfrac{1}{\beta^2} = 42.3 \qquad \beta = .154$$

$$\gamma = \dfrac{1}{\sqrt{1 - \beta^2}} \cong \dfrac{1}{1 - \dfrac{1}{2}\beta^2}$$

$$= \dfrac{1}{1 - \dfrac{11}{931}} \cong 1 + \dfrac{11}{931} = 1.012$$

We can now complete the table:

	Momentum	Kinetic Energy	$\dfrac{1}{\beta^2}$	β	γ
Electron	$150 \dfrac{\text{Mev}}{c}$	149.5 Mev	1.00001	.9999945	300
A 200-mass meson	$150 \dfrac{\text{Mev}}{c}$	79 Mev	1.41	.826	1.78
Proton	$150 \dfrac{\text{Mev}}{c}$	11 Mev	42.3	.154	1.012

THE PHOTON AND RELATIVITY

The concept of electromagnetic radiation consisting of quantized oscillators such that $\varepsilon = h\nu$ was introduced by Planck in 1901. The special theory was developed by Einstein in 1905. Had relativity come first, the concept of the quantum of radiation would have been predicted by it naturally. That the photon was an integral part of Einstein's thinking is shown by his ready explanation of the photoelectric effect where the photon nature of radiation is evident. Let us see how the photon might originate in special relativity. Relativistic dynamics led us to the equation

$$\mathcal{E}^2 - p^2 c^2 = m_0{}^2 c^4$$

It showed us that material particles are always propagated with velocities less than that of light. In order to propagate at $v = c$, it would be necessary for the quantity $m_0 = 0$. We might then think of the "corpuscle" of light as being a particle with zero rest mass. If this were true, the equation would read $\mathcal{E}^2 = p^2 c^2$, and a relation would be established between energy and momentum for the light photon. We previously stated that this was just the relation required in electromagnetic theory to explain the pressure of light. There we needed to assume

$$\frac{\text{energy/volume}}{\text{momentum/volume}} = c$$

and now we see that the photon has

$$\frac{\text{energy}}{\text{momentum}} = c$$

i.e., $\mathcal{E} = pc$.

Let us now see what the wave description would give. An electromagnetic wave is described by $\nu\lambda = c$, where $\nu = $ frequency and $\lambda = $ wavelength. We, therefore, have the equations

$$\mathcal{E} = pc \qquad \text{particle}$$

$$\nu = \frac{c}{\lambda} \qquad \text{wave}$$

If we divide one by the other, we get $\mathcal{E}/\nu = \text{const} = p\lambda$. This constant is universal and is called h (Planck's constant). Therefore,

$$\mathcal{E} = h\nu \tag{20}$$

$$p = h/\lambda \tag{21}$$

To these equations, we could add a third since

$$\mathcal{E} = mc^2 = h\nu$$

or
$$m = \frac{h\nu}{c^2} \qquad (22)$$

These are three of the most important equations in modern physics. They express the energy momentum and mass associated with photons of light. The first equation says that energy comes in "bunches" of size $h\nu$. The second equation says that the same universal constant h determines the product of $p\lambda$ (momentum and wavelength). The third equation says that although the rest mass of a photon is zero, it must be ascribed a mass $h\nu/c^2$ when it is traveling at the speed of light. Photons cannot exist at rest. They either travel at $v = c$ and have a mass $m = h\nu/c^2$; or they do not exist, and their energy appears in some other form. In fact, light is always detected by the disappearance of photons and the appearance of their energy in some other form (e.g., the ejected electron in the photoelectric effect).

We shall now take examples of these equations.

The Relation $\mathcal{E} = h\nu$

Experiments to be described later show that $h = 6.6 \times 10^{-27}$ erg-sec or $h = 4.12 \times 10^{-15}$ ev-sec. (The quantity h has the units of *action*, which is defined as px or $\mathcal{E}t$, where $p =$ momentum, $x =$ displacement, $\mathcal{E} =$ energy, and $t =$ time). What is the quantum energy for a visible photon of wavelength 6,000 Å?

$$\mathcal{E} = h\nu = \frac{hc}{\lambda} = \frac{4.12 \times 10^{-15} \; 3 \times 10^{10}}{6 \times 10^{-5}} = 2.0 \text{ ev}$$

Visible light delivers its energy in *quanta* with energy 2 ev. If the expression $\mathcal{E} = hc/\lambda$ is expressed so that $\mathcal{E}$ is in ev and λ is in Å, then

$$\mathcal{E} = \frac{12{,}345}{\lambda}$$

Actually, the constant is only correct to the first three figures, but the 12,345 makes it easy to remember.

Formally, Eq. 21 tells one the momentum that must be ascribed to a photon of wavelength λ. De Broglie suggested that perhaps material particles of momentum p also had an equivalent wavelength associated with them. This brilliant suggestion has been amply confirmed by experiment and makes the wave–particle dualism complete. The equations for a material particle that correspond to Eq. 20, 21, and 22 are

$$\mathcal{E}^2 = p^2c^2 + m_0{}^2c^4 \tag{20a}$$

$$p = \frac{h}{\lambda} \tag{21a}$$

$$m = \gamma m_0 c^2 \tag{22a}$$

De Broglie's hypothesis indicates that properly chosen electrons or atoms may be diffracted in the same way as light. Because the wavelengths are so short, a very small grating spacing is required to produce diffraction. This is supplied by the closely spaced atoms in a crystalline metal. The figure below shows the experiment.

In a typical experiment with gold, $S = 15.8$ cm, and the radius of the principle diffraction ring is .431 cm for electrons of 36,500 ev

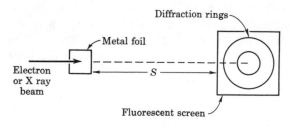

FIGURE 26

energy. The measured wavelength of these electrons from this diffraction experiment is 6.4×10^{-10} cm. Let us calculate it from De Broglie's hypothesis.

For our case

$$\gamma = \frac{m_0 c^2 + T}{m_0 c^2}$$

$$\gamma = \frac{5 \times 10^5 + 3.65 \times 10^4}{5 \times 10^5} \ 1.074$$

$$\beta^2 = 1 - \frac{1}{\gamma^2} = .13$$

$$\beta = .36$$

$$p = \gamma\beta m_0 c = 1.074(.36)5 \times 10^5 \frac{ev}{c}$$

$$= 1.93 \times 10^5 \frac{ev}{c}$$

$$= \frac{h\nu}{c} \quad \text{and} \quad \nu = \frac{1.93 \times 10^5}{4.12 \times 10^{-15}} = .469 \times 10^{20} \ sec^{-1}$$

$$\lambda = \frac{c}{\nu} = \frac{3 \times 10^{10}}{.469 \times 10^{20}} = 6.4 \times 10^{-10} \ cm$$

The calculated De Broglie wavelength is in exact agreement with the measured value. The first confirmation of De Broglie's hypothesis actually came from the diffraction of electrons by metallic crystals. It was observed at ~50 ev by Davisson and Germer in 1925.

We could ask what energy X rays are required to produce the same diffraction pattern as the electrons of our previous example. Using

$$\mathcal{E} = \frac{12{,}345}{\lambda} = \frac{12{,}345}{6.4 \times 10^{-2}}$$

gives 1.93×10^6 ev as the quantum energy. Would there be any detectable difference between the electron-diffraction pattern

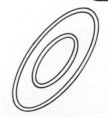

Normal electron
or X ray pattern

Electron pattern
with magnetic field

FIGURE 27

and that produced by the X rays of the same wavelength? If the diffraction is in a vacuum with no fields present the answer is no. However, the electrons are charged, whereas the photons are not. The presence of an electric or magnetic field between the specimen and the fluorescent screen will distort the electron-diffraction pattern but not the X ray pattern as in Fig. 27.

The Relation $m = h\nu/c^2$

The fact that the photon has a mass means that it is subject to gravitation. This is, properly speaking, in the domain of the general theory of relativity. In our brief discussion of this subject we will show that the mass of the photon leads to two calculable effects which we will estimate there. These effects are:

1. The deflection of light in a gravitational field (the field of the sun).
2. The change in frequency (or color) of a light photon falling or rising through a gravitational field.

The reader may already guess the nature of the calculations. They are given in Chapter 3.

THE DOPPLER EFFECT

When we considered the Doppler effect for sound, we found it was asymmetrical in the motion of the source and observer. Because of relativity, the light case must be reciprocal, because there is no distinction between source and observer moving. We now derive the relativistic case for a plane wave moving in the direction of the x axis. What invariant principle can we use? The fundamental postulate says that the velocity is the same in all systems. Therefore, the number of waves which have left the origin since $t = t' = 0$ must be the same in both systems. This is the same as saying that the phase of the wave is invariant. If the wave is given by

$$y = \cos 2\pi\nu \left(\frac{x}{c} - t\right) \qquad \text{then} \qquad \nu \left(\frac{x}{c} - t\right)$$

is invariant. To make this more specific

$$\nu \left(t - \frac{x}{c} \right)$$

is the number of waves which have left the origin after $t = 0$ and up to the moment t have reached a point a distance x from the origin. This invariance leads to

$$\nu \left(t - \frac{x}{c} \right) = \nu' \left(t' - \frac{x'}{c} \right)$$

or $\qquad\qquad \nu(ct - x) = \nu'(ct' - x')$

Using Eq. [L$_{1b}$] and [L$_{4b}$],

$$ct' = \gamma(ct - \beta x)$$

$$x' = \gamma(x - \beta ct)$$

we get $\qquad \nu(ct - x) = \nu'(1 + \beta)\gamma(ct - x)$

or $\qquad\qquad \nu = \nu'\gamma(1 + \beta)$

or $\qquad\qquad \nu = \nu' \dfrac{(1 + \beta)^{1/2}}{(1 - \beta)^{1/2}}$

Therefore, $\qquad \nu\sqrt{(1 - \beta)} = \nu'\sqrt{1 + \beta}$ $\qquad\qquad$ (23)

This transformation may be inverted by exchanging the primed and unprimed quantities and changing the sign of β. The equation is unchanged. Consider a numerical example. It has been recently reported by R. Minkowski that a galaxy has been observed to be receding from the earth at a $\beta = \frac{1}{2}$. What should be the characteristics of its light? We consider this problem in the following:

Spectral lines have a certain fundamental frequency ν_0 when they are emitted by atoms at rest. We assume that this natural frequency is the same in the receding galaxy as on the earth (this assumption which, of course, has not been proven is an example of what is called the "universal cosmological principle"). In our derivation we, as observers, are in the Σ' system, and β is $+$ if the motion is recession; ν' is the frequency we observe and

$$\nu' = \nu_0 \frac{\sqrt{1-\beta}}{\sqrt{1+\beta}}$$

For $\qquad \beta = \frac{1}{2} \quad \nu' = \nu \frac{\sqrt{\frac{1}{2}}}{\sqrt{\frac{3}{2}}} = \frac{\nu}{\sqrt{3}}$

Since $\qquad \nu'\lambda' = c \qquad \lambda' = \frac{c}{\nu'}$

and $\qquad\qquad\qquad \lambda' = \sqrt{3}\,\lambda_0$

Since the wavelength we observe is λ', we see it is longer (redder) than the natural wavelength λ_0. The expanding universe in which all galaxies recede from each other, therefore, leads to "red shifts" for the light. These are observed, and, in the case we took, the wavelength would be increased by a factor of 1.7.

LIGHT IN MATERIAL MEDIA

We have seen that relativity explains the propagation of light in a vacuum. One must, however, be able to explain certain properties of light in dielectric objects such as glass. We shall make some statements in this section which we will not prove because of the complexity of the mathematics. In discussing material media, we find we must introduce three velocities. These are the signal velocity, the phase velocity, and the group velocity. The signal velocity is always equal to the speed of light in a vacuum, i.e., c. The phase velocity is the velocity with which a pattern is propagated. The phase velocities combine together to give the group velocity at which the energy or a pulsed signal is propagated. When an electromagnetic disturbance is propagated in a material medium the resultant disturbance is the sum of the initial disturbance and that produced by the secondary waves emitted by the electrons in the medium. The signal velocity c is the velocity with which these electrons can communicate with each other.

The result of their radiation superimposed on the incident radiation sets up a wave pattern which determines such features of the medium as the index of refraction. Because the index of refraction is measured by a geometrical feature (for example, by the angles in Snell's law), it is determined by the phase velocity of the wave produced by interference between the primary wave and all the secondary waves arising from each electron. This phase velocity sets up a geometric pattern and the phase velocity may be greater or less than the velocity of light. (It is usually less than the velocity c for visible light in media such as glass or water. It is greater than c for X rays propagated through metals.) Since energy is not propagated with this velocity, it may be greater or less than c. When the phase velocity is known, the group velocity is given by $\mu = v - \lambda \, dv/d\lambda$, and this is the velocity at which the energy is transmitted. The group velocity is always less than or equal to c by the principle of relativity. To take an example, we consider the measurement of the velocity of light in CS_2 made by Michelson. The phase velocity may be determined by using refraction (Snell's law). This leads to an index of refraction $n = c/v = 1.64$. Maxwell's theory also actually predicts the correct value of the phase velocity as $v = c/\sqrt{k\mu}$, where k is the dielectric constant, and μ the permeability (each, of course, measured at the appropriate frequency). Because of the dispersion of CS_2, the index of refraction corresponding to the group velocity is $n_g = c/\mu = 1.77$. Michelson's measurement shows $n = 1.77$ for the measurement of the transmission of a pulse of light through the medium. We believe, however, that in setting up the microscopic phenomena, the individual electrons are able to communicate with each other through empty space with the signal velocity c. That is, we believe that, if we had detectors of unlimited sensitivity, we could measure a pulse coming through the CS_2 at a velocity c. In several of the problems we shall see how special relativity may be applied formally to the propagation in material media. The answers we get are in agreement with more exact calculations which follow the arguments given above, but the formal application of the transformation equations to these problems does not give an understanding of the complete physical picture.

THE TWIN PARADOX

Before leaving special relativity, we must mention a famous "paradox" which arose in special theory. It is a problem that may be approached by the special theory. We shall state it first in a paradoxical way. Suppose two twins perform the following experiment. One twin, R, stays on earth; the other, M, gets on a rocket ship and travels away at high speed. After some time, M turns around and returns to earth. During the trip each thinks that the other's clock is running slow. What will they find when they compare clocks? They can't both be slow!! We shall see that with certain assumptions relativity predicts that the clock on earth will show more elapsed time — in fact γ times more. In other words, we are led to the remarkable conclusion that the twin in the rocket ship might come back and find his brother dead. We now give the solution from the standpoint of special relativity with the Minkowski diagram and using the Lorentz transformation.

Consider an observer R at rest at the origin O of the inertial system Σ. A second observer M is at first to be at rest at the same point O and is then to move off with uniform velocity along a straight line — say, the $+x$ axis — until he has reached a point x where he is to turn around and return to O along a straight line with the same velocity.

The solutions of the problem fall into one of the following classes.

Einstein Class (a)

These solutions are based on the special theory of relativity but assume that the observer M *may be distinguished* from the observer R. The events are events at which M is present but R is not. The events referred to are M's coming to rest, reversing direction, and returning to the origin. The Minkowski diagram for this type of solution is given in Fig. 28, for

$$\beta = \frac{v}{c} = \frac{3}{5} \quad \text{and} \quad \gamma = \frac{1}{\sqrt{1-\beta^2}} = \frac{5}{4}$$

The coordinate system Σ contains R at its origin, and Σ' and Σ'' contain M at their respective origins on the outward and return

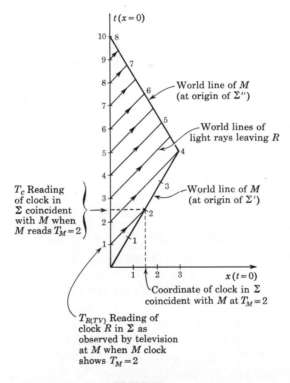

FIGURE 28

journeys, respectively. In Fig. 28 we plot the world line of M, showing in addition, the light signals which connect R and M. In Fig. 29 we show a plot of coordinate times in Σ, (T_c) as well as the time shown on the origin clock at R as observed by M on a television screen. This time is called $T_{R(TV)}$. We also plot the x coordinate of the Σ clock showing the coordinate time. The units are chosen so that $c = 1$.

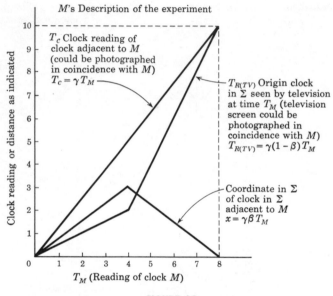

FIGURE 29

Figure 30 shows the predicted result to be obtained by photographing the clock at M, the television screen, and the coordinate clock (together with its x coordinate) at $T_M = 2$.

It can be seen that solution a gives a relative retardation of the M clock. If the total duration of the journey as shown by R's clock is $2T$, then the duration as shown by M's clock is $2T/\gamma$, as obtained by Einstein and others. It has been claimed by some that this solution is the unique relativistic solution.

Dingle Class of Solutions (b)

Dingle asserts that the principle of relativity shows that it is impossible to state that M in the above example is the accelerated observer, and that in our solution we could equally well have assumed that R was the accelerated observer (with respect to M) and, therefore, that A's and not M's clock is retarded. Obviously

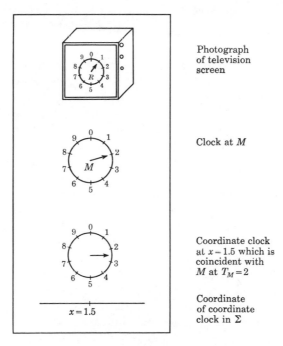

Photograph of television screen

Clock at M

Coordinate clock at $x=1.5$ which is coincident with M at $T_M=2$

Coordinate of coordinate clock in Σ

$x=1.5$

FIGURE 30

both cannot be retarded, so Dingle is always able to show that any solution of the type dictated by a will lead to both clocks showing the same elapsed time if we accept the hypothesis that acceleration is only relative in the two systems.

Detailed Model Solutions (c)

These solutions are based on the assumption that one must describe the exact process by which observer M or R is turned around. One may assume, for example, that the system containing

M is reversed by a rocket or by an elastic collision, etc. These solutions give a relative retardation as in class a, if one assumes that M is the system to which something happens.

"General Relativistic Solutions" (d)

These ascribe the asymmetry to a gravitational field, uniform in space, which observer M substitutes for his acceleration. These solutions also give the relative retardation as in a but do not explain why observer R does not feel the gravitation which M invokes to make R's clock "race ahead" during M's acceleration. These solutions are purely formal, artificial, and redundant since they use the principle of equivalence to substitute an artificial gravitational field for the acceleration. We shall show in a later section that the role of the equivalence principle in general relativity is to allow the calculation of the effect of gravitation by substituting a calculation on the basis of special relativity in the equivalent accelerated system. Using the equivalence principle in solutions of type d is the same as using it twice, first to get gravitation by substituting an equivalent accelerated system (as in Einstein's classic solution of the red-shift problem), and then using it again to make the system of the twin problem appear to be a problem in gravitation, which need not be so unless the mechanism of the acceleration is indeed gravitation.

In the twin problem in the real universe, twin M must be assumed to have the acceleration and solutions of class a giving a relative retardation are correct. If we assumed that twin R had the acceleration, *we would also have to assume that all the rest of the universe is likewise accelerated.* We would then face the same problem that arises if we assume that the earth's rotation is replaced by a counterrotation of the rest of the universe.

On the other hand in a "massless" universe containing only R and M, the principle of relativity as stated by Dingle would apply, and both observers would obtain the same time. In this case the only interactions in the universe would be between M and R, and we could tie them together with a spring or their own gravitation, for example.

The solutions of class c apply to real physical problems in the actual universe and, therefore, correctly give relative retardations as in class a.

An example of a solution of class c follows. An experiment which could be performed (if its result were really in doubt) may make the situation clearer. A beam of μ mesons may be produced at a γ of at least 10 in the Berkeley Bevatron. Such a beam could be split into two parts, one part is stopped in matter, the other is trapped in a magnetic field. The rate at which mesons decay in each circumstance can be measured, and certainly those at high γ will decay with a 10 times longer half-life. After some time, they may also be stopped, and the number of survivors can be compared with those surviving from the ones originally stopped. The mesons which were kept at high γ will contain more survivors. We illustrate this numerically in Fig. 31 below.

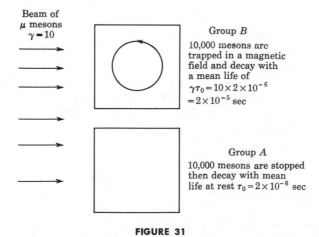

Beam of
μ mesons
$\gamma = 10$

Group B
10,000 mesons are trapped in a magnetic field and decay with a mean life of
$\gamma \tau_0 = 10 \times 2 \times 10^{-6}$
$= 2 \times 10^{-5}$ sec

Group A
10,000 mesons are stopped then decay with mean life at rest $\tau_0 = 2 \times 10^{-6}$ sec

FIGURE 31

Neglecting the statistics in the finite number of mesons, if we stop the group B after time t and compare A survivors with B survivors, we would get the following results:

Time of stopping Group B and comparing survivors, t	A Survivors	B Survivors
2×10^{-6} sec	4,000	9,000
4×10^{-6} sec	1,350	8,000
6×10^{-6} sec	500	7,000

In this example we see that the mesons in the accelerated system live longer, just as we saw in the twin problem, where on final comparison of the clocks, the twin in the accelerated system found his clock showed less elapsed time.

EXPERIMENTAL TESTS OF THE SPECIAL THEORY

Almost every nuclear physicist tests special relativity every day. High-energy cosmic-ray physicists use the Lorentz transformation with the same confidence that prerelativity physicists used Newton's laws. In examining the tests of relativity one concludes that the relativistic predictions are verified with almost whatever accuracy the experimenter is able to obtain. The only relativistic prediction which has not been verified directly is the Lorentz contraction, although the relativistic velocity addition has not been measured to great enough accuracy to distinguish between classical and relativistic values. We cannot give all the experiments which confirm relativity but will list at least one under the various predictions.

Time Dilatation

The lifetime of μ and π mesons, accelerated, or present in cosmic rays, follows the prediction $\tau = \gamma \tau_0$. τ_0 is the proper rest lifetime, and τ the lifetime observed for mesons in flight. This law has been tested with high accuracy at low energies and with approximately 10 percent accuracy at γs as high as 100.

Lorentz Contraction

Although this has not been verified directly there is indirect evidence that it does exist. A direct consequence of the contraction is the change in shape of the coulomb field of a charged particle in motion. The electrostatic field of a point charge at rest is spherically symmetrical. Observed at high γ, this field is weakened in the direction of motion and strengthened at right angles to this. In experiments where this effect has to be taken into account, the relativistic calculations seem correct. We do not consider this a direct test, however.

Relativistic Increase in Mass

The first experiment to measure $m = m_0/\sqrt{1 - \beta^2}$ was that of Bucherer in 1909. It has since been performed on electrons and other particles with greater accuracy. The formula is tested to an accuracy of better than 0.1 percent. The experiment consists of deflecting high-energy particles in a magnetic field. The energy is known from the accelerating potential, and the transverse momentum per unit of charge is measured by deflection in a magnetic field. The proof of $m = \gamma m_0$ rests on the assumption that the charge does not change. We have given arguments that convince us that the charge does not depend on velocity (see page 65).

The Relativistic Mass-Energy Relation

The relation $\varepsilon = mc^2$ is tested in every nuclear reaction. It is also tested by the binding energy of nuclei. The accuracy of $\varepsilon = mc^2$ is at least confirmed to one part in 10^5. A spectacular example of this relation is the case of proton-antiproton creation and electron-pair creation (see Probs. 24 and 28). In these cases (particle creation) large quantities of matter and energy are interchanged. The belief in $\varepsilon = mc^2$ is so firm that the $7 million Berkeley Bevatron was designed for just the energy required to produce proton-antiproton pairs. The calculation of the required energy was confirmed when these particles were created and observed for the *first time* with this machine. The nuclear bombs, both fission and fusion, utilize the energy release predicted by $\mathcal{E} = mc^2$.

The Velocity-Addition Theorem

Since we cannot accelerate ourselves at the present time into a frame of high γ, we must test the velocity addition by experiments which depend on it. The experiments are the aberration of light due to the earth's orbital motion and the Fresnel dragging coefficient, which produces a change in the velocity of light in a moving dielectric medium (see Probs. 49 and 52). These experiments give results consistent with either the classical ether theory or relativity, and so they are not conclusive. The velocity-addition theorem follows so directly from the Lorentz transformation that it can hardly be in doubt if the other predictions of the special theory are verified. A recently discovered phenomena "the Mossbauer effect" should make it possible to test the velocity-addition theorem in the laboratory.

Relativistic Doppler Effect

The difference between the classical and relativistic Doppler effects are summarized by the equations which describe them (see Probs. 15, 16, and 17).

Classically for a stationary ether

$$\nu = \nu_0 \frac{(1 \mp \beta_1)}{(1 \pm \beta_2)}$$

β_2 refers to the source motion and β_1 to the observer motion. The upper signs refer to motion of separation and the lower signs to motion of approach. ν_0 is the source natural frequency.

Relativistically

$$\nu = \nu' \frac{(1 + \beta \cos \Theta')^*}{\sqrt{1 - \beta^2}} \qquad \nu' \text{ is the emitted frequency in } \Sigma', \text{ i.e., } \nu_0.$$

* The angle of emission in Σ' and observation in Σ are related by the law of aberration

$$\cos \Theta = \frac{\cos \Theta' + \beta}{1 + \beta \cos \Theta'} \qquad \text{for } \Theta = \frac{\pi}{2} \qquad \cos \Theta' = -\beta$$

β refers to the velocity of the relative motion, Θ' is the angle of emission of the light in the system in which the source is located. If $\cos \Theta' = -1$ (backwards emission in Σ') then

$$\nu = \nu_0 \frac{(1 - \beta)}{(1 - \beta^2)^{1/2}} \approx \nu_0 (1 - \beta) \qquad \text{red shift}$$

the case we have considered in the text.

The differences in relativity are:

1. Independence of source or observer motion.
2. Second-order Doppler effect at right angles to the motion, whereas none should exist classically. This effect is $(\cos \Theta' = -\beta)$.

$$\nu_T = \frac{\nu_0}{\gamma} \approx \nu_0 \left(1 - \frac{1}{2} \beta^2 \right) \qquad \text{red shift also}$$

Both predictions (1) and (2) are verified by the observation of moving atoms in the laboratory. The classic experiment establishing the relativistic result was carried out by Ives and Stilwell* who observed the light emitted by hydrogen atoms moving toward their detector. By placing a mirror behind the beam, they could simultaneously photograph the forward and backward emitted light. In this case the center of gravity of the wavelengths of the forward and backward light is shifted by the second-order Doppler effect (see Probs. 58 and 59). The predicted shift is shown in Fig. 32 where it is seen that the second-order shift displaces the center of gravity of the forward- and backward-emitted spectral lines.

In the experiment of Ives and Stilwell both first- and second-order Doppler effects are measured at different velocities of the atoms. Figure 33 shows their result. Note the smallness of the second-order shift as compared with the first-order shift. The relativistic prediction is verified within 1 per cent by experiment. Nonrelativistically, there should be no second-order Doppler shift, and the magnitude of the second-order shift has been measured with an accuracy of about ± 1 per cent.

---

* H. E. Ives and G. R. Stilwell, "An Experimental Study of the Rate of a Moving Atomic Clock," *J. Opt. Soc. Am.*, *XXVIII*, no. 7, (July, 1938), 215.

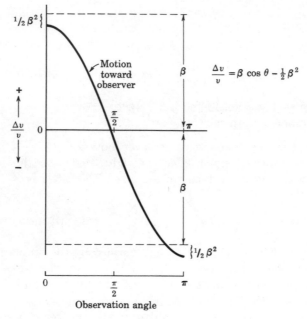

$$\frac{\Delta v}{v} = \beta \cos \theta - \tfrac{1}{2}\beta^2$$

FIGURE 32

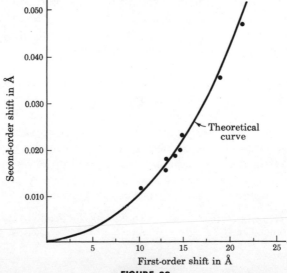

FIGURE 33

CHAPTER 3. The General Theory of Relativity

Einstein developed the restricted theory of relativity in 1905. In 1911 he published a paper entitled "On the Influence of Gravitation on the Propagation of Light." In this paper he attempted to formulate the problem of relativity with gravitation and proposed his famous equivalence principle. He predicted the relativistic red shift of spectral lines and calculated the gravitational deflection of light in the vicinity of matter.* Finally, in 1916, in a paper, "The Foundation of the General Theory of Relativity," he formulated the complete theory and calculated the red shift, the gravitational deflection of light, and the precession of the perihelion of mercury. The first two papers, (1905) and (1911), should be read by any serious student of relativity. They are written in German, but an excellent translation is available in *The Principle of Relativity*. The last-quoted paper is more

---

* His value of the red shift was correct, but he obtained a value for the gravitational deflection of light which was too small by a factor of 2. This was because the theory at this time was incompletely applied, as we shall see.

mathematical than the first two, and we shall try to translate its content into physical terms avoiding the tensor mathematics. Einstein proposed his cosmological model in 1917 in a paper, "Cosmological Considerations of the General Theory of Relativity." This theory predicts a finite radius for the "seeable" universe, and we shall calculate the size of the Einstein universe in the last part of this section. We shall now discuss some experimental and conceptual ingredients of the general theory. The first subject is the relationship of inertial and gravitational mass, as established precisely by Roland v. Eötvös during the period 1890–1922. It should be pointed out that as Minkowski has said of Einstein's theories, they "have sprung from the soil of experimental physics, and therein lies their strength." The experiment on which the special theory was built was the Michelson-Morley experiment, and the equivalence principle of general theory depends on the result of the Eötvös experiment.

INERTIAL AND GRAVITATIONAL MASS AND THE
NEWTON, BESSELS, EÖTVÖS EXPERIMENTS

In 1700, when Newton formulated his laws of motion, he realized that they involved the assumption of the equivalence of gravitational and inertial mass. When gravitation acts on a body, it acts on the "gravitational mass," but the result of the force is an acceleration of the "inertial mass." The fact that all bodies fall with the same acceleration indicates that within the accuracy of the experiment the ratio of inertial to gravitational mass is independent of the body. If this ratio is constant, we can adjust our units so that $m_g = m_i$ where $m_g =$ gravitational mass and $m_i =$ inertial mass. In the gravitational case we would write

$$m_{i1}a_1 = \frac{GM}{R^2} m_{g1} \cong m_{g1}g$$

$$m_{i2}a_2 = \frac{GM}{R^2} m_{g2} \cong m_{g2}g$$

If $a_1 = a_2$, then $\dfrac{m_{i1}}{m_{g1}} = \dfrac{m_{i2}}{m_{g2}}$

and our assertion is proved. However, the accuracy with which the masses are equal is determined with only the accuracy by which we show that $a_1 = a_2$. Newton was able to show that, if there was a difference between inertial and gravitational mass, it was not greater than one part in 1,000 (his accuracy in measuring a_1/a_2). In the following we shall use the quantity x to indicate the fractional amount by which inertial and gravitational masses could differ. Newton showed that

$$x < \frac{1}{1,000}$$

Bessels observed that the periods of pendulums made of different materials offered a more sensitive test of the equivalence. The period T should be:

$$T = 2\pi \sqrt{\frac{m_i}{m_g} \frac{l}{g}}$$

By measuring the periods of pendulums of equal lengths at the same place (g is the same), Bessels showed that

$$x < \frac{1}{6 \times 10^4}$$

R. v. Eötvös* used an extremely ingenious method to set the limit more precisely. To understand his

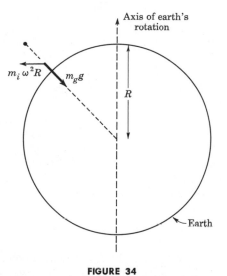

FIGURE 34

method, consider a pendulum hanging at a latitude of 45° as shown in Fig. 34.

It can be seen from this figure that the direction of the pendulum

* R. v. Eötvös, D. Pekár, and E. Fekete: "Beiträge zum Gesetze der Proportionalität von Trägheit und Gravität," *Ann. Physik, LXVIII* (July, 1922), 11.

will not be toward the center of the earth but in the direction of the resultant of the forces $m_i w^2 R$ and $m_g g$. If e is the angle between the direction of the pendulum and the direction to the center of the earth,* then e is a simple function of m_i/m_g. Eötvös used a null method to compare the ratio m_i/m_g for different objects. His equipment consists of a torsion pendulum, as shown with the

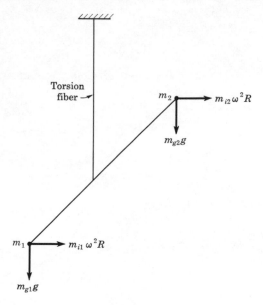

FIGURE 35

forces on the bobs indicated in perspective in Fig. 35 (see Prob. 60).

By orienting the axis $m_1 m_2$ north, south, east, and west successively and observing the twist in the torsion fiber with a mirror

---

* The angle e is, of course, very small (see Prob. 60). Also the direction of g is not truly toward the center of the earth but is the local direction of g, which is somewhat determined by the structure and density of the earth near the observing point. In fact, the Eötvös pendulum determines this direction so well that it is used in oil prospecting.

and microscope, any inequality of m_{i1}/m_{i2} for equal values of m_{g1}/m_{g2} may be determined. Eötvös and his collaborators established that $x < (1/2) \times 10^{-8}$. Eight different materials (including tallow, wormwood, and more conventional substances, such as water and copper) were compared with platinum. It was established that chemical reactions did not change the result and the experiment was also carried out by comparing a radioactive source with platinum. In the case of the radioactive material, the accuracy was less by a factor of 100 because of the small size of the

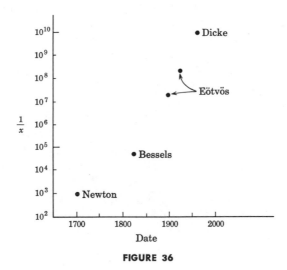

FIGURE 36

sample. In Fig. 36 the result of the experiments we have described is plotted as a function of time. The apparent improvement in the Eötvös experiment (between 1890 and 1922) comes from increasing the number of observations from several to several hundred in each position of the balance. Dicke* has redone the Eötvös experiment using modern techniques and reports that $x < 1/10^{10}$.

* R. H. Dicke, *Scientific American*, (December, 1961), 84.

NEWTON'S AND EINSTEIN'S IDEAS ABOUT ROTATION

Newton believed in absolute rotation. In support of this idea he gives the following example. Suppose a pail of water is hung by a rope and set into rotation. The surface of the water is at first flat until it partakes of the rotation of the pail. It then takes on a parabolic shape, showing the effect of centrifugal forces. Newton takes this as evidence for rotation with respect to an absolute frame, i.e., absolute rotation. The same effect is evidenced in the equatorial bulge of a rotating planet. However, the presence of this absolute frame is uncheckable except in terms of this experiment; i.e., the experiment is what leads to the concept of absolute rotation, and the "proof" of absolute rotation is the result of the experiment. Consider the example of Fig. 37. Bodies A and B are in rotation relative to each other about the axis OO'. Suppose A and B to be far separated in the universe. In this relative rotation which body (or both) will suffer the equatorial bulge? Einstein would contend that in a matter-free universe neither would show the bulge. However, we cannot do experiments in a matter-free universe, and we are led to the conclusion that the appearance of centrifugal forces is caused by the effect of all the distant matter in the universe, which is on the average at rest with respect to the rotating object. We may view this as a rotation of the object with respect to the distant matter or conversely as rotation of the distant matter with respect to the object. In other words the presence of gravitating matter "does something" to the spacetime continuum.

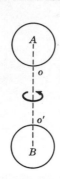

FIGURE 37

THE EQUIVALENCE PRINCIPLE

We now consider a different kind of experiment. Suppose we are inside a closed elevator weighing two masses with spring balances. If the elevator is at rest on the surface of the earth the masses will weigh m_1g and m_2g. Now suppose the elevator to be accelerated downward with an acceleration $\frac{1}{2}g$. The observer will see that the masses weigh $m_1 g/2$ and $m_2 g/2$. However, the same result would have been obtained if the elevator had been placed at rest on another planet where the effective gravity was just $g/2$. We cannot distinguish the difference between gravitation and acceleration. According to Einstein, they are, therefore, equivalent; and this reasoning leads to the "equivalence principle" which may be stated as follows:* The effect of gravitation can in no way be distinguished from the effect of acceleration; each is fully equivalent to the other. This principle is the basis of the equality of gravitational and inertial mass which was established with such high accuracy by von Eötvös. To take another example: Consider an observer in a box on the surface of the earth. He is aware of a force that the box exerts on him; (he could measure it with a spring scale). Now suppose gravity were turned off but the force remained. The box would shoot off into space with an acceleration of g, but the observer would be unaware of any change because his spring scale would still read the same. We shall see how the equivalence principle above, together with a knowledge of special relativity allows us to derive results which are identical with those obtained by application of the general theory. We might now ask: If gravitation and acceleration cannot be distinguished, is it not possible to transform away all gravitation by going to the proper accelerated system? The answer, in general, is no. We can transform away gravitation in a limited region of space time but not everywhere. The simplest case to consider is the gravitation of the earth. By going to a system whose angular

---

* Einstein's own statement refers to two systems K and K', where K is in a gravitational field and K' is far away from matter but is uniformly accelerated: "We arrive at a very satisfactory interpretation of this experiment, if we assume that the systems K and K' are physically exactly equivalent, that is if we assume that we may just as well regard the system K as being in a space free from gravitational fields, if we then regard K as uniformly accelerated. This assumption of exact physical equivalence makes it impossible for us to speak of the absolute acceleration of the system of reference, just as the usual theory of relativity forbids us to talk of the absolute velocity of a system; and it makes the equal falling of all bodies in a gravitational field seem a matter of course."

velocity is ω and observing that

$$a = \omega^2 R = \frac{GM}{R^2}$$

we can see that, by choosing $\omega^2 = GM/R^3$, we can transform away the gravitation at a radius R. (This is Kepler's law in a somewhat different connotation.) However, the transformation will only transform away gravitation at the radius R, and more or less gravitation will be present at other radii. Einstein, therefore, formulated a theory in which space time is described in Gaussian coordinates which vary depending on the distribution of matter. This formulation not only strikes at our intuitive ideas about physics but also disavows Euclidean geometry. The idea of a straight line of Euclidean geometry is a concept which cannot be checked except by comparison with the "straightness" of a light ray. To see if a meter stick is straight, we might sight along it. In the general theory the ray of light travels on a "geodesic" in space time. This is equivalent to the two-dimensional case of a sphere where the great circles represent the geodesics but are manifestly not straight lines.

One simple example will show how relativity must imply a different geometry (in general) than Euclidean. Consider a region of space time in which there is no gravitation. Embed a coordinate system Σ in space time. Now consider a body which is rotating with respect to Σ at an angular velocity ω. This will be the system Σ'. Let observers in Σ, Σ' determine the characteristics of the rotating disk. We must note that because of the rotation and the equivalence principle, a gravitational field exists in Σ'. This field is directed radially outward and has the value $g = \omega^2 r$. The observer in Σ' says the "gravitation" is stronger the greater the radius r. In the figure below a larger force is required to balance the gravitation at the radius r_2 than at r_1. Suppose the observer in Σ wishes to express the ratio of the circumference to the diameter of the circle. If we call $\pi = 3.14$ and if he requires 100 m-sticks to measure the diameter, he will require 314 to measure the circumference. Now use special relativity and transform to the Σ' system. In measuring the diameter (since the motion is at right angles to this), the Σ' observer requires 100 sticks; but to measure the circumference (because of the motion of Σ') he will require more than 314 because his meter stick is shortened by the factor γ. In fact, he will measure different values of π depending on the radius, because the velocity is proportional to the radius. However, so is g, and he will therefore conclude that the geometry (in this case the value of π) depends on g. A similar result holds for clocks. Clocks in Σ' will run slow, and the amount they run slow will depend on the value of g which the Σ' observer ascribes to the point in question. A clock at the periphery runs slower than one halfway out because the velocity of the periphery is greater.

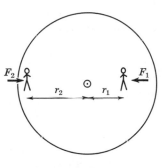

FIGURE 38

We shall now briefly outline Einstein's formulation of the general theory. The mathematics, however, are complicated, and we shall follow this outline with numerical calculations which are particularly simple and which will not require the complete formalism of the general theory.

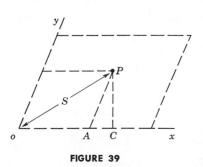

FIGURE 39

The mathematics of Einstein's formulation had been worked out previously by Gauss (1827) and by Reimann. The coordinates to describe geometry (even on curved surfaces) are called Gaussian coordinates. They are not in general Cartesian coordinates. In the figure above we represent a portion of a grid in two-dimensional space. The coordinates of the point P

in this system are shown. We assume that the measure or metric along x and y need not be the same. It can be shown that the distance S is given by

$$S^2 = a^2x^2 + 2acxy + b^2y^2$$

where the true length along $x = ax$

the true length along $y = by$

the true length of $AC = cy$

(PC is perpendicular to OC.) This equation is usually written as

$$S^2 = g_{11}x^2 + 2g_{12}xy + g_{22}y^2$$

The factors g_{11} and g_{12} and g_{22} are called the *factors of measure determination.* Now S^2 is the geometrical line element or the ground invariant G of relativity. If we express the relativistic line element in four-space in Gaussian coordinates, it is

$$S^2 = G = g_{11}x^2 + g_{22}y^2 + g_{33}z^2 + g_{44}t^2 + 2g_{12}xy$$
$$+ 2g_{13}xz + 2g_{14}xt + 2g_{23}yz$$
$$+ 2g_{24}yt + 2g_{34}xt$$

This formula is the generalized Pythagorean theorem for the four-dimensional world. The task of general relativity is, therefore, to calculate the gs which will depend on the distribution of matter. The gs determine the metric or the gravitational field. In particular, if no gravitational field is present (special relativity), then

$$g_{11} = g_{22} = g_{33} = 1 \qquad g_{44} = -c^2$$
$$g_{12} = g_{13} = g_{14} = g_{23} = g_{24} = g_{34} = 0$$

We see that this reduces to the ground invariant

$$G = x^2 + y^2 + z^2 - c^2t^2$$

of special relativity. The more general equation in which all the gs may have values is the invariant in general theory. The quantity g_{44} has special significance. If T_0 is the natural period of a clock, then its period as observed in space time will be

$$T = T_0 \frac{c}{\sqrt{-g_{44}}}$$

If the space is fieldless, then $g_{44} = -c^2$ and $T = T_0$. However, if there is gravitation, $g_{44} \not\sim -c^2$ and $T \not= T_0$, as we saw in our example of the rotating coordinate system.

We now proceed to make some calculations which do not depend on the intricacies of the general theory but which show the strength and importance of the principle of equivalence.

CLOCKS IN A GRAVITATIONAL FIELD

Consider two observers A and B who are in a *constant* gravitational field g but are separated a distance l. The field is directed as indicated. The drawing below shows that this is equivalent to no gravitation and an acceleration $a = g$, as indicated (equivalence principle).

Suppose light from an atomic transition is emitted at A and observed at B. The light has natural frequency ν_0 and natural

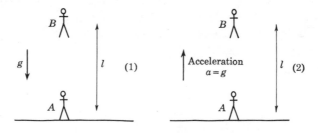

FIGURE 40

period T_0. What will observer B see? We can analyze this by using the situation (2) which is equivalent to (1). The time it takes light to travel from A to B is $t = l/c$. During this time, both observers being accelerated will acquire a velocity $v = at = gt = gl/c$. Since the light was already emitted, we can ignore A, and we only care about the velocity of B when he receives the light. This velocity v is $v = gl/c$. Now, since he is moving away from the source, he will see a red shift as we have pointed out and will by the Doppler principle see light of frequency

$$\nu' = \nu_0 \frac{(1 - \beta)}{\sqrt{1 - \beta^2}}$$

This expression can be simplified to

$$\nu' = \nu_0 \left(1 - \beta + \frac{1}{2} \beta^2 + \cdots \right)$$

Since the higher-order term may usually be neglected,

$$\nu' \approx \nu_0(1 - \beta) = \nu_0 \left(1 - \frac{gl}{c^2} \right)$$

and the period

$$T = \frac{1}{\nu'} \cong T_0 \left(1 + \frac{gl}{c^2} \right)$$

We see that in passing up through the gravitational field the light has become redder. Since red light has less energy than blue light, we might consider the previous problem from the standpoint of photons. We have seen that the photon has energy $\mathcal{E} = mc^2$. The work it does against the gravitational field is reflected in a change in this energy. If we assume that the only way the photon may change its energy is by changing its mass (and since its mass is $mc^2 = h\nu$), the change in mass produces a change in frequency. Let us write the equations

$$\mathcal{E} = mc^2$$
$$\Delta \mathcal{E} = mgl = -\Delta mc^2$$
$$\frac{\Delta m}{m} = -\frac{gl}{c^2}$$

and $\quad \dfrac{\Delta \nu}{\nu} = \dfrac{\Delta m}{m} = -\dfrac{gl}{c^2} \quad$ or $\quad \nu' = \nu_0 \left(1 - \dfrac{gl}{c^2} \right)$

This is exactly the answer we got before. Both cases were written for the photon moving against the gravitation. Light falling in a gravitational field gains energy and becomes bluer.

The remarkable prediction above has been verified experimentally by Pound and Rebka (1960).* They were able to measure the change in color of light in falling a distance of 60 ft in the earth's gravitational field. This is a remarkable achievement. The $\Delta\nu/\nu$ for this case is only $\Delta\nu/\nu = 2 \times 10^{-15}$. In spite of this, they verified the relativistic prediction with good accuracy. Their result is

$$\frac{\text{Measured shift}}{\text{Theoretical shift}} = +1.05 \pm 0.10$$

Since all of the light that comes from stars must escape from rather strong gravitational fields, much larger shifts are expected than that in the experiment of Pound and Rebka. It is left as a problem for the student to show that for light leaving a star, the change in frequency is given by

$$\frac{\Delta\nu}{\nu} = -\frac{GM}{Rc^2}$$

where

$G =$ the universal constant of gravitation

$M =$ the mass of the star

$R =$ its radius

$c =$ the velocity of light

There is some evidence that the gravitational red shift has been observed for light emitted by white dwarfs which are stars with densities 10,000 times greater than ordinary matter.

Deflection of Light in the Gravitational Field of a Star

In 1801 a German mathematician named Soldner calculated the deflection of light in the gravitational field of the sun. His result which we reproduce here leads to the prediction of a deflection of

* R. V. Pound and G. A. Rebka, Jr., "Letters," *Phys. Rev.*, IV, (1960) 337.

.87 seconds of arc. Shortly after developing the general theory, Einstein calculated the deflection and got the same answer. However, he later further developed the theory and found that general relativity actually predicts a value twice this large or 1.75 seconds of arc. The experiment was first performed in 1919, and the result reported was 1.7 seconds of arc. The experiment is difficult, and more recent experiments have not agreed as well with theory as the 1919 experiment. This prediction of the theory can only be considered to be confirmed to an accuracy of perhaps 20 percent. The procedure of the experiment is to photograph a star field around the sun during a total eclipse (so that the stars are visible). Six months later, when the same stars are visible at night, the star field is photographed again. The displacement of the apparent positions of the stars can be measured by comparing the two photographs.

Soldner's Derivation

The transverse momentum P_1 imparted to an object of mass m can be shown to be given at point P (see Fig. 41) by

$$dP_\perp = \frac{GMm}{cR} \cos \Theta \, d\Theta$$

The total transverse momentum is

$$P_\perp = \int dP_\perp = \int_{\Theta=-\pi/2}^{\Theta=\pi/2} \frac{GMm}{cR} \cos \Theta \, d\Theta = \frac{2GMm}{cR}$$

The angle φ is

$$\varphi = \frac{P_\perp}{P} = \frac{\dfrac{2GMm}{cR}}{mc}$$

and, therefore,

$$\varphi = \frac{2GM}{c^2R} \text{ radians}$$

Substitution in this formula for the case of the sun leads to the "classical" value of $\varphi = 0.87$ seconds of arc. Note that, although the mass of the photon cancels out in the derivation, the mass must be finite, i.e., $m \neq 0$; and this was not established in prerelativity physics. It should also be emphasized that Soldner's value is only half the correct value given by the general theory.

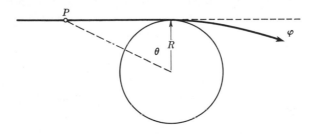

FIGURE 41

EXPERIMENTAL TESTS OF THE GENERAL THEORY

Because the effects predicted by the general theory are very small, they are difficult to establish experimentally. However, the so-called crucial tests of the theory have been confirmed with reasonable accuracy. They are the following:

Precession of the Perihelion of Mercury

When Einstein's general theory is applied to the solar system, the result is that Newton's laws are found to give the same orbits with high accuracy. In order to see deviations from Newton's laws, we have to take planetary orbits that are near the sun. The planet which best satisfies this condition is the planet Mercury. In the case of Mercury most of the advance (precession) is caused by the perturbing effect of other planets, especially Venus. The precession due to these perturbations can be calculated by Newtonian mechanics with adequate precision.* The result is a predicted precession of 5,557.2 seconds of arc per century. The measured value is 5,599.7 seconds of arc per century. This difference had puzzled astronomers for 50 years.

* Although only the two-body problem is soluble, many-body problems may be approximately solved by splitting them into successive two-body problems.

One of the suggestions to account for the "anomalous" precession was that the sun's equatorial diameter might exceed its polar diameter. If there were a .028 percent difference in the diameters, the precession would be accounted for. However, it was shown that such a difference would also lead to a change in the inclination of Mercury's orbit of 3 sec/century. A value this large could be, but has not been, detected. Therefore, some — but not all — of the anomalous precession could be explained by the shape of the sun.

Einstein showed that general relativity predicts an added precession of 43 seconds of arc per century. We see that the anomalous precession as measured is 42.5 seconds of arc per century. The astronomical data on Mercury's orbit has been carefully studied by G. M. Clemence.* He shows that the precession produced by the solar oblateness (see Probs. 55, 56) is negligible because of the nonuniform density of the sun. He concludes that the anomalous precession as measured is 42.56 ± .94, and the relativistic prediction is 43.03 ± .03. The agreement appears to be excellent. In the last section we shall show how the relativistic precession may be calculated.

The Gravitational Red Shift

The astronomical measurements of this quantity have not been convincing. The reason for this is that the gravitational shift is masked by large and uncertain Doppler shifts. This effect has, however, been established with high accuracy (within several per cent) by the experiment of Pound and Rebka on light falling in the earth's gravitation. Unfortunately the red shift is not a true test of the general theory but only of the principle of equivalence. One will recall that all that was required to derive the red shift was this principle together with special relativity.

Deflection of Light in a Gravitational Field

We have shown Soldner's argument for the deflection of light in a gravitational field. In the next section we shall calculate the

* G. M. Clemence, "Relativity Effect in Planetary Motions," *Rev. Modern Phys.* XIX, no. 4, (October, 1947) 361.

relativistic value. The "classical" value, which ignored the relativistic effects of gravitation, gave an answer only half as large as the correct general relativistic answer. We discuss this experiment in some detail because of its importance and also to emphasize the very small deviations which are the result of general relativity.

The experiment to be performed is the measurement of a star field with the sun in the center, and the same field without the sun. In order to measure a star field with the sun present, we must have a total eclipse. Eclipses last only up to seven minutes, and occur every several years; so the observation time is severely limited. The eclipse photograph must be compared with the same field at night. This requires a second experiment with the same equipment some months earlier or later (so that the stars may be seen at night). To see them in the same place, one could observe 6 months later at night.

During the interval between the experiments, the magnification must remain constant because the effect being studied is very similar to just a change in magnification. The entire magnitude of the effect for a star at the limb of the sun could be simulated by a change in magnification of one part in 500. To measure the effect to within .1 seconds of arc (the standard deviation quoted in the best measurements), we need a constancy in magnification or scale to about one part in 10^4. In the most recent experiments (since 1947) the scale has been fixed by simultaneously photographing a star field away from sun and comparing this star field in the two experiments to establish the scale. Because of the extreme difficulty of the experiment, the systematic errors are much larger than the errors indicated by the consistency of the data. Also, the measurements are based on relatively few stars. Unfortunately, no eclipse has occurred in the milky way. For example, in the 1929 eclipse 18 stars were used, but a diameter could be drawn so that 17 of these fell on one side of it. The experiment has been performed without obvious experimental troubles 10 times in the interval between 1919 and 1959. The results are summarized in Fig. 42, where individual measurements are indicated by equal areas, the width of which are given by the standard deviation quoted by the observer.

One can see from this figure that many of the results cluster

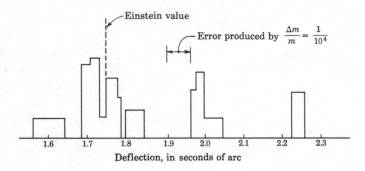

Deflection, in seconds of arc

FIGURE 42

around the Einstein value, but some are quite far away. The measurement by Michailov in the 1936 eclipse is 2.71 ± 0.26, over 1.5 times the predicted value. The reader can judge for himself how well the prediction of the general relativity is verified.

CHAPTER 4. Calculation of the General Relativistic Effects

The three predicted effects produced by Einstein as consequences of the general theory are:

1. The perihelion precession
2. The deflection of light in a gravitational field
3. The relativistic red shift

Whether these so called "crucial tests" really verify or even test the general theory is somewhat in doubt. Although the idea for the general theory came from the "equivalence principle," there is much more to the general theory than the equivalence principle plus special relativity. In what follows, however, we shall derive the relativistic values for (1), (2), and (3), using only the equivalence principle and special relativity. The fact that this can be done makes one distrust these phenomena as real tests of the general theory. In addition to obtaining values for (1), (2), and (3), we shall derive some results concerning the velocity of light near gravitating bodies. An advantage of our elementary derivation is that we can see what the contribution of the various relativistic effects is to (1), (2), and (3).

DERIVATION OF THE TRANSFORMATION RULE

The equivalence principle states that the effect of gravitation cannot be distinguished from the effect of an acceleration. We wish to compare the metric at a position r away from a gravitating object with the metric in an inertial system far away from gravitating matter. The effect of the gravitation is to produce an acceleration $a = GM/r^2$, and a velocity v such that $\frac{1}{2}mv^2 = GMm/r$,* assuming that β is small. β is then given by

$$\beta^2 = \frac{2GM}{rc^2} = \frac{2\alpha}{r}$$

The meaning of the quantity α (gravitational radius) is emphasized in Probs. 38 and 39. If we calculate the lengths and times in a system with velocity βc as compared with our inertial system at infinity, these lengths and times will correspond to those that apply at rest in the gravitational field at radius r. It is clear that from the Lorentz transformations the relations will be

$$dr = \frac{dx}{\gamma} = \sqrt{1 - \beta^2}\, dx \cong \left(1 - \frac{\alpha}{r}\right) dx$$

$$ds_\Theta = dy$$

$$ds_\varphi = dz$$

$$dt_g = \gamma\, dt = \frac{1}{\sqrt{1 - \beta^2}}\, dt \cong \left(1 + \frac{\alpha}{r}\right) dt$$

In writing these equations, we have taken the x axis along the direction of r, and the distances ds_Θ and ds_φ are perpendicular to x and to r. We arrive at the remarkable conclusion that the result of the gravitation is to make:

Lengths in the radial direction shrink by a factor of γ
Lengths in the tangential direction stay the same
Clocks run slow by a factor γ when these quantities are compared with an inertial system away from gravitation.

---

* We really should have written $(m - m_0)c^2 = GMm/r$ but if β is small our expression is all right.

We can, therefore, make a prescription for determining the effects of general relativity on a problem for which the solution is known (from Newtonian mechanics). The rule is: Take the Newtonian solution and substitute

$$\text{For} \quad r_0 \to r_0 \left(1 - \frac{\alpha}{r} \right)$$

$$T_0 \to T_0 \left(1 + \frac{\alpha}{r} \right)$$

$$r_\perp \to r_\perp$$

$$M_0 \to M_0 \left(1 + \frac{\alpha}{r} \right)$$

We shall apply this procedure to derive the magnitudes of the relativistic effects (1), (2) and (3), and to determine the velocity of light in a gravitational field.

We have seen that the "transformation rule" leads to a change in the Newtonian-Euclidean metric which is fractionally always of the order of α/r. In our part of the universe, this is always small, and approximations like

$$\frac{1}{\sqrt{1 - \frac{\alpha}{r}}} \to 1 + \frac{1}{2} \frac{\alpha}{r}$$

are valid since they are correct up to terms in $(\alpha/r)^2$. To indicate the magnitude of α/r, we show a table including the largest values encountered. The table shows the gravitational radius α of the sun, Jupiter, and the earth and the values of α/R at surface of the object.

Celestial object	Gravitational radius, α	$\dfrac{\alpha}{R_0}$
Sun	1.4 km	2.4×10^{-6}
Jupiter	1.25 m	2.2×10^{-8}
Earth	0.4 cm	$7 \ \times 10^{-10}$

THE VELOCITY OF LIGHT NEAR A GRAVITATING MASS

Because the lengths and time are changed, the velocity of light near gravitating matter is different than in a gravity-free inertial system. It is always less near gravitating matter and has different values in different directions.

The velocity of light in the radial and tangential directions is given by:

$$v_r = \frac{dr}{dt} = \frac{dx}{dt} \frac{\left(1 - \dfrac{\alpha}{r}\right)}{\left(1 + \dfrac{\alpha}{r}\right)} = c_\infty \left(1 - 2\,\frac{\alpha}{r}\right)$$

The radial velocity of light near gravitating matter is less fractionally by $2\alpha/r$ than its value at ∞ where no gravitation is present.

The tangential velocity v_t is given by

$$v_t = \frac{dx_\Theta}{dt} = \frac{dx_\varphi}{dt} = c_\infty \left(1 - \frac{\alpha}{r}\right)$$

The tangential velocity is less than the value at infinity because, although the tangential lengths are unchanged, the clocks run slow.

In spite of the above results, there is a kind of implied constancy of the velocity of light in the presence of gravitation. An observer using a conventional method for measuring the velocity will obtain the same value near the gravitating mass as at infinity. Let us imagine that the velocity is "measured" in the following way. The observer is equipped with a clock, a light source, and a meter stick as shown in Fig. 43.

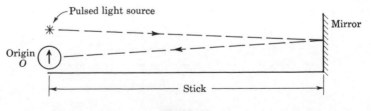

FIGURE 43

The observer may orient the stick in any direction and may make his observations at infinity or in the gravitational field. Consider the comparison of the clock reading when the experiment is performed at infinity and in the gravitational field. Let n_∞, n_T, and n_r be the number of divisions on the clock between the emission of the pulse of light at O and its return. Then:

$$n_\infty = \frac{2L_\infty}{c_\infty T_\infty}$$

$$n_T = \frac{2L_T}{c_T T_T} = \frac{2L_\infty}{c_\infty \left(1 - \dfrac{\alpha}{r}\right) T_\infty \left(1 + \dfrac{\alpha}{r}\right)} = \frac{2L_\infty}{c_\infty T_\infty}$$

$$n_R = \frac{2L_R}{c_R T_R} = \frac{2L_\infty \left(1 - \dfrac{\alpha}{r}\right)}{c_\infty \left(1 - \dfrac{2\alpha}{r}\right) T_\infty \left(1 + \dfrac{\alpha}{r}\right)} = \frac{2L_\infty}{c_\infty T_\infty}$$

In other words, the velocities, lengths, and times have changed in just the right way to make an observation of the velocity of light give the same value regardless of the presence or absence of gravitation and regardless of the direction in which the measurement is performed. Fizeau's measurement of the velocity of light would give the same result on the surface of the sun as on the surface of the earth. It seems that in general relativity as in special relativity a measurement of the velocity of light always yields the same result regardless of the motion of the observer or of the presence or absence of gravitation. The change in the metric can be observed, however, by the bending of light in the sun's gravitation where we see that the velocity does depend on the magnitude of the gravitation, i.e., on the value of α/r.

THE PRECESSION OF THE PERIHELION

We shall calculate the precession first for a circular orbit. The fact that an orbit "precesses" is just another way to say that the particle gets around the orbit faster. We will, therefore, calculate the angle which a planet turns through in one period by pure

Newtonian mechanics. The angle relativistically calculated will be obtained by appropriately changing radial lengths, etc. The difference between the relativistic value and the Newtonian value is the "relativistic precession."

Newtonian Result

$$m\omega^2 r = \frac{GMm}{r^2}$$

So

$$\omega^2 = \frac{GM}{r^3} \qquad \omega = \frac{(GM)^{1/2}}{r^{3/2}}$$

$$\Theta_N = \omega T = \frac{(GM)^{1/2}}{r^{3/2}}\, T$$

where the angle Θ is the angle turned through in one period T.

The relativistic value is obtained by substitution:

$$T_r = T\left(1 + \frac{\alpha}{r}\right)$$

$$r_r = r\left(1 - \frac{\alpha}{r}\right)$$

$$M_r = \frac{M}{\sqrt{1 - \beta^2}} = M\left(1 + \frac{\alpha}{r}\right)$$

So

$$\Theta_r = \frac{(GM)^{1/2}}{r^{3/2}}\, T\, \frac{(1 + \alpha/r)(1 + \frac{1}{2}\alpha/r)}{(1 - \frac{3}{2}\alpha/r)}$$

$$\Theta_r = \Theta_N\left(1 + 3\,\frac{\alpha}{r}\right)$$

$$\Theta_r - \Theta_N = \Phi = 3\,\frac{\alpha}{r}\,\Theta_N$$

$$\Theta_N = 2\pi$$

because one period is the time elapsed; therefore,

$$\Phi = 6\pi\,\frac{\alpha}{r}$$

The quantity Φ, as calculated, agrees with the Einstein value; and consideration of our transformation shows that the fraction of the precession produced by each effect is given below. F is the fraction:

Quantity	F
Change in radial metric....	1/2
Change in time	1/3
Relativistic mass	1/6

If the orbit is elliptical then the quantity $1/r$ must be replaced by $(1/r)$ average. The minimum and maximum distances for the ellipse are

$$\frac{1}{r_{\min}} = \frac{1}{a(1 - e)} \qquad \frac{1}{r_{\max}} = \frac{1}{a(1 + e)}$$

Therefore,

$$\frac{1/r_{\min} + 1/r_{\max}}{2} = \frac{1}{2}\frac{1}{a(1 - e)} + \frac{1}{2}\frac{1}{a(1 + e)} = \frac{1}{a(1 - e^2)}$$

The complete expression is, therefore,

$$\Phi = \frac{6\pi\alpha}{a(1 - e^2)}$$

Substitution of the values for Mercury (planet):

$$\alpha = 1.4 \text{ kM}$$
$$a = 58 \times 10^6 \text{ kM}$$
$$e = .20$$

leads to a value of 43 seconds of arc per century. In checking this, observe that Φ is per period, and the period of Mercury is 88 days.

For the earth, because of the larger a, Φ is smaller, and the value calculated is $\Phi = 3.8$ seconds of arc per century.

THE DEFLECTION OF LIGHT IN A GRAVITATIONAL FIELD

In the text we worked this problem for a photon and got an answer for the deflection $\varphi = 2\alpha/a$ where a is the radius at which

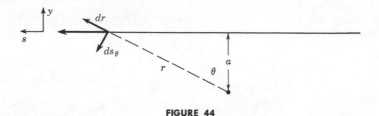

FIGURE 44

the light passes the sun. This answer was too small because it does not properly account for the change in the metric. We shall

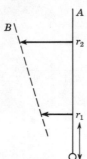

FIGURE 45

reformulate the problem so that we may take all of the effects into account. The bending of the light is produced because of the variation of the velocity with position and direction. Consider a wave front passing the sun. The wave front A advances to B and is bent because the velocity at r_1 is less than the velocity at r_2.

In our first figure we must calculate the $\partial v / \partial y$ because this determines the angle of deflection. It is easy to see that

$$\varphi = \int \frac{\partial v}{\partial y} \frac{1}{v} \, ds \cong \int \frac{\partial v}{\partial y} \frac{1}{c} \, ds$$

$$v_r = c \left(1 - 2 \frac{\alpha}{r} \right) \qquad \text{Therefore,} \qquad \frac{\partial v_r}{\partial r} = \frac{2\alpha c}{r^2}$$

$$v_\theta = c \left(1 - \frac{\alpha}{r} \right) \qquad \text{and} \qquad \frac{\partial v_\theta}{\partial s_\theta} = \frac{\alpha c}{r^2}$$

Therefore,

$$\frac{\partial v}{\partial y} = \frac{\partial v_\theta}{\partial s_\theta} \sin \Theta + \frac{\partial v_r}{\partial r} \cos \Theta$$

or $\qquad \dfrac{\partial v}{\partial y} = \dfrac{\alpha c}{r^2} \sin \Theta + \dfrac{2\alpha c}{r^2} \cos \Theta$

Thus, $\qquad \varphi = \displaystyle\int_{-\infty}^{\infty} \frac{\alpha}{r^2} (\sin \Theta + 2 \cos \Theta) \, ds$

$$s = a \tan \Theta \qquad ds = a \sec^2 \Theta \, d\Theta$$

$$r^2 = \frac{a^2}{\cos^2 \Theta} = a^2 \sec^2 \Theta$$

and so $\quad \varphi = \frac{\alpha}{a} \int_{-\pi/2}^{\pi/2} (\sin \Theta + 2 \cos \Theta)\, d\Theta$

The $\sin \Theta$ integrates to zero, and the angle φ is

$$\varphi = \frac{\alpha}{a} \int_{-\pi/2}^{\pi/2} 2 \cos \Theta\, d\Theta = \frac{4\alpha}{a}$$

This is the correct relativistic value which leads to 1.8 seconds of arc with $\alpha = 2.4 \times 10^{-6}$ and $a =$ solar radius.

It is interesting to note that our derivation shows that the deflection really arises from the radial variation of the velocity of light; the part coming from the tangential variation integrates to zero.

THE RED SHIFT

We have shown that clocks run slow in a gravitational field and that their period is lengthened in the ratio of $(1 + \alpha/r)$. Since the frequency of light just measures the rate of a clock, we see directly that

$$\frac{\Delta f}{f} = -\frac{\alpha}{r} = -\frac{\Delta\lambda}{\lambda}$$

and the light emitted in the gravitational field is reddened. This is very analogous to the effect verified by Pound and Rebka in which light emitted at one gravitational potential is observed at another gravitational potential. From the standpoint of the general theory, it is not correct to think of the photon losing or gaining energy in the gravitational field but, instead, to consider that the basic "clocks" run at different rates.

EINSTEIN'S COSMOLOGY

We can use the ideas of this section to derive Einstein's cosmology. He showed with the general theory that, if a universe exceeded a certain size, matter and light could not escape from it. This radius of the universe depends on the gravitational constant and the density of the universe.

On our model we will ask, "How large must a universe be in order that it shall contain light emitted within it?" We have shown that the metric of space depends on α/r, and the size of the "seeable" universe will correspond to $\alpha/r \to 1$. In our calculation of the bending of light near the sun, we saw that the angle of deflection was given to first order by $\tan \varphi \approx \varphi \approx 4\alpha/r$; so very large deflections occur if $\alpha/r \to 1$. Let us be more quantitative. We calculated the radial and tangential values of the velocity of light near gravitating matter and found that at a radius R from a spherical source the velocities were

$$v_R = c_\infty \left(1 - 2\frac{\alpha}{R}\right)$$

$$v_T = c_\infty \sqrt{1 - 2\frac{\alpha}{R}}$$

We can see then that the velocity of light will be reduced to zero if $\alpha/R = \frac{1}{2}$. The light will go around in geodesics inside this radius R.

The condition $\alpha/R = \frac{1}{2}$ leads to the following

$$\frac{\alpha}{R} = \frac{1}{2} = \frac{GM}{c^2 R} = \frac{1}{2}$$

If we assume* that $M = \frac{4}{3}\pi R^3 \rho$ we arrive at the conclusion

$$\frac{1}{R^2} = \frac{\frac{8}{3}\pi G\rho}{c^2}$$

And, for the mass of the universe, we obtain

$$M = \frac{c^2 R}{2G}$$

---

* Einstein uses more general geometry so this volume is given by a somewhat different expression. The volume in Einstein's space is $V = 2\pi^2 R^3$.

In the table below we list our elementary values and those obtained by Einstein.

	Our values	Correct general relativity values
Radius....	$\dfrac{R^2}{c^2} = \dfrac{1}{\dfrac{8}{3}\pi G\rho}$	$\dfrac{R^2}{c^2} = \dfrac{1}{4\pi G\rho}$
Mass	$M = \dfrac{c^2 R}{2G}$	$M = \dfrac{\pi}{2}\dfrac{c^2 R}{G}$

Finally, it is interesting to study Einstein's predictions on the basis of astronomical information. The density of matter in intergalactic space is now believed to be 1/1,000 of a hydrogen atom/cm^3. We get, therefore, for ρ, $\rho \cong 10^{-27}$ g/cm^2. R/c is the radius of the universe in light seconds

Therefore

$$\left(\frac{R}{c}\right)^2 = \frac{1}{4\pi(6.7 \times 10^{-8})(10^{-27})}$$

$$\frac{R}{c} = \frac{1}{3} \times 10^{17} \text{ light seconds} = \frac{10^{17}}{3\pi \times 10^7} \text{ light years}$$

or $\quad \dfrac{R}{c} \cong 10^9$ light years

There seems to be evidence, now, from the 200-in. telescope that this may be approximately the real size of the observable universe.

Knowing the radius, we can calculate the mass of the universe, and we get $M \cong 4 \times 10^{54}$ g. Since there are 6×10^{23} protons and an equal number of electrons in a gram of hydrogen, we conclude that there are approximately 5×10^{78} particles (electrons and protons) in the universe.

In the previous discussion we have used the "cosmological condition" $\alpha/R = \frac{1}{2}$ to show that light is contained within the radius R, and that, therefore, R represents the radius of the "seeable" universe. The cosmological condition may have an even deeper meaning. Let us write it in the following form.

$$\frac{\alpha}{R} = \frac{1}{2} = \frac{GM}{Rc^2} \quad \text{is the same as} \quad mc^2 = \frac{2GMm}{R}$$

The rest mass energy of a mass m is equal to twice the gravitational potential energy of this mass with respect to all the rest of the mass in the universe. We might, therefore, assume (as Mach did) that the inertial and gravitational masses arise because of the rest of the mass in the universe. This has led to some interesting speculation. If the condition $\alpha/R = \frac{1}{2}$ is always true, then $GM/Rc^2 = $ constant.

If the universe is expanding,* then its radius is a function of the time,

$$R = \text{const } t$$

and the assumed constancy of GM/Rc^2 would imply that G, M, or c, or a combination of these, changes with time. We must, therefore, not assume that the constants of nature have always been the same and search for evidence which bears on the possible variation of any of these quantities with time.

In closing this section, we quote Max Born!

Different people find progressive abstraction, objectivization, and relativization easy or difficult as the case may be. The older peoples of the continent, Dutch, French, Germans, Italians, Scandinavians are most susceptible to these ideas, and are most deeply involved in elaborating this system. Englishmen, who incline to concrete ideas, are less readily accessible. Americans are fond of attaching themselves to mechanical pictures and models. Even Michelson whose experimental researches had the greatest share in destroying the ether theory, repudiates a theory of light without the ether as unthinkable. But the younger generation is already being educated in the sense of the new ideas and accepts as self-evident what was regarded by the older school as an unheard of innovation.

We hope that the reader now belongs to the latter class.

* Hubble has shown that the red shift of distant galaxies is proportional to their distance. He finds a value for $h = $ velocity/distance of between 14 and 25 if the velocity is expressed in cm/sec and the distance in light years. The quantity $1/h$ is a time, and is sometimes considered the age of the universe. For $h = 14$, the time is 2.1×10^9 years, and for $h = 25$, it is 1.2×10^9 years.

CHAPTER 5. Problems on Relativity

Problem 1. The combined effect of surface tension and gravity waves on water can be expressed by the equation for the velocity $v^2 = g\lambda/2\pi + 2\pi T/\rho\lambda$, where $T =$ the surface tension, $\rho =$ the density, $g =$ the acceleration of gravity and $\lambda =$ the wavelength.

(a) Show that the velocity has a minimum given by $v_0 = (4Tg/\rho)^{1/4}$.

(b) Show that the value of the wavelength for the minimum velocity is $\lambda_0 = 2\pi(T/g\rho)^{1/2}$.

(c) Show that the minimum velocity for water waves is 23 cm/sec. This velocity is equal to about .5 miles/hr. This is the reason that, for low-velocity winds (less than .5 miles/hr), no waves or ripples appear and the surface of a body of water is dead calm.

Problem 2. Using the concept of photons, show that the radiation pressure on a black surface is equal to the energy density in the light beam.

Problem 3.   Show that the force due to radiation pressure on a black sphere is the same as the force on a shiny sphere.   *Note:* If they were flat plates oriented perpendicular to the beam, there would be a factor of 2 difference.

Problem 4.   (*a*) Calculate the radiation pressure on the earth assuming that the solar constant has a value of 2 cal/cm^2 min at the earth.

(*b*) Compare this with the solar gravitation for a black earth. To get the gravitational attraction, do not use M_{sun} and G. The earth-sun distance is 98×10^6 mi. Mass of earth $= 6 \times 10^{24}$ kg.

(*c*) What is the ratio of the acceleration of gravity at earth's surface to the acceleration produced by the solar attraction.

Answer: (*a*) 5×10^{-5} dynes/cm^2.   (*b*) Ratio is 1.5×10^{-14}. (*c*) Ratio is 1.6×10^3.

Problem 5.   It has been suggested that particles smaller than a given critical size would be blown out of the solar system by radiation pressure. Show that this would be true independent of distance from the sun and calculate the critical size assuming that the particles have a density of 1 and absorb all of the energy falling on their cross section.

Answer: 6,700 Å.

Problem 6.   Compare the collision of a photon with a black surface and the collision of a putty ball (which sticks to the surface).

(*a*) Assume that the energy of the photon and the kinetic energy of the putty ball are the same and show that the ratio of the momentum transferred is $R = 2c/v$ if $\beta \to 0$. R is the ratio of momentum transferred by the putty ball to the momentum transferred by the light.

(*b*) Assume that the putty ball and the light have the same total energy and show that in this case R becomes $R = \beta$. Discuss the result.

Problem 7. A problem related to the Michelson-Morley experiment is the following: An airplane travels from A to B in still air in a time t. The speed of the airplane is c.

(a) Compare the time t with the round-trip time when a wind of velocity $v < c$ blows from A to B.

(b) Compare with the time required when the wind is blowing perpendicular to AB.

Answer: $t_1 = 2\dfrac{l}{c}$, (a) $t_a = (2l/c)(1 + \beta^2)$, (b) $t_b = (2l/c)(1 + \tfrac{1}{2}\beta^2)$.

Problem 8. Show that the Lorentz contraction can be derived by assuming that the Σ observer measures the time interval between the passing of his origin by the two ends of the meter stick in Σ'. The length in Σ is obtained by multiplying this time interval by v.

Problem 9. Show that the time dilatation may be obtained by measuring the distance in Σ between two events occurring at the origin of Σ' and dividing this distance by v to get the time interval in Σ.

Problem 10. Σ, Σ' synchronize clocks at origin. After 10 min by his clock, Σ looks through a telescope at Σ'. What does he see Σ's clock read if $\gamma = 2$.

Answer: 2.7 min.

Problem 11. Oscilloscope manufacturers claim writing speeds in excess of the velocity of light. Is this possible? Explain.

Problem 12. Calculate the radius of curvature of a 100-Mev electron in a magnetic field of 10,000 gauss.

Answer: 33 cm.

Problem 13. If the general magnetic field in the solar system is 2×10^{-5} gauss, what fraction of the earth-sun distance is the radius of curvature of a 400-Mev proton; (400-Mev kinetic energy).

Answer: Radius = 1/100 earth-sun distance.

Problem 14. In observations on a charged particle it is established that its value of $1/\beta^2 = 2$ (from ionization measurements). Its radius of curvature is 46 cm in a magnetic field of 10,000 gauss. What is its mass?

Answer: 270 m_e.

Problem 15. *Longitudinal Doppler Shift.* For a source receding along the line of sight of an observer, the Doppler shift is given by $\nu = \nu_0\gamma(1 - \beta)$, where $\nu_0 =$ the natural frequency and $\nu =$ the observed frequency. Show that this expression follows from the time dilatation and the motion of the source.

Problem 16. *Transverse Doppler Shift.* In relativity there is a transverse Doppler shift. A source observed at right angles to the motion shows a shift $\nu = \nu_0/\gamma \cong \nu_0(1 - \frac{1}{2}\beta^2)$. Use the ideas of the preceding problem to prove this.

Problem 17. *First- and Second-Order Doppler Effects*

(a) Show that the first-order Doppler effect is given approximately by $\nu = \nu_0(1 - \beta + \frac{1}{2}\beta^2)$, or if β is small $\nu \cong \nu_0(1 - \beta)$, and that the transverse Doppler effect has no β term and is given by $\nu \cong \nu_0(1 - \frac{1}{2}\beta^2)$.

(b) Calculate the longitudinal and transverse Doppler shifts for $\beta = \frac{1}{4}$.

Answer: (b) $\nu_L = \frac{3}{4}\nu_0$ $\nu_T = \frac{31}{32}\nu_0$.

Problem 18. We showed the triangle relating $\mathcal{E}$, p, and m_0c^2 in normalized units. Show the same triangle in ordinary units and also in terms only of β and γ.

Problem 19. Make a computer to solve the following equations using only a sheet of Cartesian graph paper, a pair of scissors, and one pin: $\mathcal{E}^2 = p^2 + 1$, $p/\mathcal{E} = \beta$, $\mathcal{E} = T + 1$. The computer need only cover the range $p = 0$ to $p = 3$.

Problem 20. Using a computer, as in the previous problem, led to the following values. The computer was set at the value of

PROBLEMS ON RELATIVITY **129**

β, and p, and ε determined.   Calculate the correct values of ε

β	.9	.6	.3
ε	2.22	1.24	1.04
p	2.0	.74	.32

and p, and determine the average error made with the computer.

Answer: Error is 2 per cent.

Problem 21.   Show that $pc/\varepsilon = \beta$ for a free particle.

Problem 22.   Show that for i interacting particles the coordinate system in which the total momentum (vector) is zero (called the center of mass systems) is moving with a velocity $\beta_{cm}c$, where $\beta_{cm}c$ (velocity of the center of mass) is given by

$$\beta_{cm} = \frac{\Sigma_i p_i c}{\Sigma_i \varepsilon_i}$$

Problem 23.   Consider two identical interacting particles. In the laboratory one particle is at rest, the other has β_L, γ_L. If β_{cm} and γ_{cm} refer to the center of mass system, show that

$$\beta_{cm} = \frac{\beta_L \gamma_L}{1 + \gamma_L} \quad \text{and} \quad 2\gamma_{cm}^2 = \gamma_L + 1$$

Problem 24.   The Berkeley Bevatron was designed to produce proton-antiproton pairs by bombarding stationary protons with high-energy protons.   The nuclear physicist would write this $p + p \rightarrow p + p + (p + \bar{p})$.   Each particle has rest mass $m_0 c^2$, so $2m_0 c^2$ units of rest mass must be created.   Use the ideas of the preceding problems to calculate the kinetic energy required in the laboratory system in order that the reaction may go.   (This is called the threshold energy.)

Answer: $6M_0 c^2$, where $M_0 c^2$ is rest-mass energy of a proton. (*Hint:* Solve the problem in the *CM* system and transform back.)

Problem 25. Consider the previous problem (Bevatron) in the following way.

In Lab

For the bombarding particle:
$$\mathcal{E} = p^2 c^2 + m_0^2 c^4 \tag{1}$$

In CM

$$\mathcal{E}_1 + \mathcal{E}_2 = 4 m_0 c^2 \tag{2}$$

$$\mathcal{E}_1 = \mathcal{E}_2 = \left(\frac{p}{2}\right)^2 c^2 + m_0^2 c^4 \tag{3}$$

Solving (2) and (3) for p and substituting in (1) gives $p^2 c^2 = 12 m_0^2 c^4$ and $\mathcal{E} = 3.6 m_0 c^2$ or $T = 2.6 m_0 c^2$. The correct answer is $6 m_0 c^2$. What is wrong with the above approach?

Problem 26. Show that if $\beta \to 1$, the fractional difference between v and c is $\frac{1}{2}(m_0 c^2 / \mathcal{E})^2$.

Problem 27. Show that, if $\mathcal{E}$ and p are expressed in normalized units, the Lorentz transformation has the same form as the x, t transformation, i.e.,

$$p'_x = \gamma(p_x - \beta \mathcal{E})$$
$$p'_y = p_y$$
$$p'_t = p_z$$
$$\mathcal{E}' = \gamma(\mathcal{E} - \beta p_x)$$

Problem 28. *Pair Annihilation.* In space a positron and an electron can combine at rest and annihilate. The positron is a positive particle with mass equal to the electron. In the process two γ rays are emitted. Describe such a process in which energy and momentum are conserved, and calculate the wavelength of the γ rays. Note that charge is conserved also.

Problem 29. "Two clocks properly synchronized are at points A and B of the system Σ. The clock A is moved with the velocity v along the line AB to B, then on its arrival at B the two clocks no longer synchronize, but the clock moved from A to B lags behind the other which has remained at B by $\frac{1}{2}t\,v^2/c^2$ (up to magnitudes of fourth and higher order), t being the time occupied in the journey from A to B." From Einstein's first paper on special relativity, "Zur Electrodynamik Bewegter Körper," *Annalen der Physik*, (1905) 17. Prove the above statement.

Problem 30. "If one of two synchronous clocks at A is moved in a closed curve with constant velocity until it returns to A, the journey lasting t sec; then by the clock which has remained at rest, the traveled clock on its arrival at A will be $\frac{1}{2}t\beta^2$ sec slow." Also from Einstein (1905). Prove the above statement assuming only special relativity.

Problem 31. "We conclude that a balance clock at the equator must go more slowly, by a very small amount, than a precisely similar clock situated at one of the poles under otherwise uniform conditions." Also from Einstein (1905). Calculate the difference in the clocks.

Answer: Difference is 3 msec/century.

Problem 32. In some of the early literature starting with Einstein, two kinds of mass were considered. These were called transverse and longitudinal. We showed that, if $F = d(mv)/dt$, there is only one mass $m = \gamma m_0$. The transverse mass of Einstein is also given by this expression.

(a) Show that another mass: Longitudinal mass $= m_0/(1 - \beta^2)^{3/2}$ would have to be defined if we used the equation $F = ma$ instead of $F = d(mv)/dt$.

(b) Is the longitudinal mass a necessary concept?

Problem 33. *Relativistic Rocket Ship.* Consider a rocket ship in which mass can be converted into energy. Consider the best theoretical possibility for the material to be exhausted. The rocket ship is away from gravitational fields so small thrust is satisfactory. If the rocket is observed from its initial inertial frame and if $R = M_0/M$ is the mass ratio:

(a) Show that for the best case

$$R^2 = 1 + 2\beta\gamma = 1 + \frac{2\beta}{\sqrt{1 - \beta^2}}$$

(b) Check this result for the boundary conditions $R = 1$ and $R = \infty$, and calculate the value of β for $R = 2$.

Answer: $\beta = .83$.

Problem 34. The previous problem showed that it is possible to acquire high β's or γ's in principle in a relativistic rocket ship. Is it possible to travel great distances in space in human lifetimes? The closest stars are light years away. What γ is required to go one light year, as measured from the earth, in one year of time measured by the observer in the rocket ship?

Answer: $\gamma = \sqrt{2}$ and $\beta^2 = \frac{1}{2}$.

Problem 35. Our galaxy is 100,000 light years across. What γ is required to traverse this distance in 10 years?

Answer: $\gamma \doteq 10^{11}; \beta \to 1$

Problem 36. In the preceding problem, what is the mass ratio required for the relativistic rocket ship.

Answer: $R = 140$ ignoring acceleration time.

Problem 37. If a relativistic rocket ship could be made with $R = 2$ and if we could ignore the acceleration time, how many light years could one travel for every year of elapsed time?

Answer: 1.5 (light years)/year.

Problem 38. The quantity $\alpha = GM/c^2$ has the dimensions of a length.

(a) Show this. In general relativity this quantity is called the gravitational radius of the mass.
(b) Show that, if the gravitational energy were equal to the rest energy, the radius would be given by an expression like the one above.

Problem 39. It is shown in general relativity that the fractional deviation of the space metric from Euclidean is given by $\Delta S/S = \alpha/r$, where $\alpha =$ the gravitational radius of an object and $r =$ its actual radius. For example, a meter stick measured in the absence of gravitation will shrink if placed radially in a gravitational field by $\Delta S/S$.

(a) Calculate the shrinkage of a radial meter stick placed at the earth's surface,

(b) Calculate the shrinkage of the stick at the sun's surface.

Answer: (a) $\Delta S/S = 7 \times 10^{-10}$. (b) $\Delta S/S = 2.4 \times 10^{-6}$.

Problem 40. If an object has a mass of 1 g at the surface of the earth, what will be its mass:

(a) At the center of the earth?

(b) At the surface of the sun? *Hint:* Remember that gravitational and inertial masses are equal and that the deviation from the metric and mass at infinity is a function of the gravitational potential.

Answer: (a) Mass increased by 7.3×10^{-10} g. (b) Mass increased by 2.4×10^{-6} g.

Problem 41. *Gravitational Red Shift.* Consider the red shift produced upon light escaping from the gravitational field of a celestial body.

(a) Show that the fractional change in wavelength of the light which escapes from the star is $\Delta\lambda/\lambda = GM/Rc^2$, where $G =$ universal gravitational constant, $R =$ radius of the star, $M =$ its mass.

(b) Also show that, if the surface gravity of a planet is g, the same reddening will be produced in rising a distance R in this constant field as would be produced by escape from the actual gravitational field.

(c) At what distance from the star has half the reddening occurred?

Problem 42. Calculate the change in wavelength of a photon falling 60 ft in the gravitational field of the earth.

Answer: $1.9 \times 10^{-15} = \Delta\lambda/\lambda$.

Problem 43. The mass of the dense companion of Sirius is 1.7×10^{33} g. Find its density, assuming that it shows a gravitational red shift equal to the Doppler shift at 3×10^6 cm/sec.

Answer: $\rho = 2 \times 10^5$ g/cm^3.

Problem 44. Complete the steps in Soldner's derivation for the deflection of light in a gravitational field.

Problem 45. (a) Substitute the solar values in Soldner's equation to calculate the deflection expected near the surface of the sun.
(b) What would the deflection be at an elongation x equal to $x = 2R$, where $R =$ radius of the sun.

Answer: (a) 0.86 sec. (b) 0.43 sec.

Problem 46. In Soldner's derivation of the deflection of a photon in the solar gravitation, we neglected the fact that as the photon gets into the gravitational field its mass increases. $m = m_\infty(1 + \alpha/r)$, where $m_\infty =$ the mass at great distance, $r =$ the radial distance, and $\alpha =$ gravitational radius of the sun $\alpha = GM/c^2$. Show that, when this is included, the answer for the deflection is still the same, i.e., $\Theta = 2\alpha/R$, where $R =$ radial distance at which the light passes the sun. Discuss this.

Problem 47. In discussing the synchronizing of clocks, we suggested that the clocks could be synchronized at the same place and carried slowly $\beta \to 0$ to their destinations. Why must they be carried slowly? *Hint:* Equivalence principle.

Problem 48. In discussing the visual shape of rapidly moving bodies, we showed that, because of the Lorentz contraction, objects are seen rotated but undistorted. For the case of a cube, show that the contraction is just right to make the cube appear as a rotated projection; and show that the angle through which it is turned is $\sin^{-1}\beta$.

Problem 49. *Aberration of Starlight.* The apparent positions of stars change because of the motion of the earth in its orbit. Using the relativistic velocity transformation show that $\sin \Theta = \beta$ gives the angle from the normal when the motion of the earth is at right angles to the observing direction.

Problem 50. Show that in the nonrelativistic model with a stationary ether frame the aberration of starlight is given by $\tan \Theta = \beta$.

Problem 51. Calculate the aberration of starlight by the relativistic and nonrelativistic formulas, and discuss the problem of checking the result experimentally.

Problem 52. *Fresnel's Dragging Coefficient.* It has been demonstrated by Fresnel and Fizeau that a moving medium with index of refraction η produces an observed velocity $\mu = c/\eta + v(1 - 1/\eta^2)$ for light. μ is the velocity observed by the stationary observer, and v is the relative velocity of the medium in which the phase velocity of the light is characterized by the index of refraction η. The effect has been detected by measuring the velocity of light through counter-flowing water columns. Show that Fresnel's equation may be derived relativistically using the velocity transformation equations. Actually, the relativistic result is

$$\mu = \frac{c/\eta + v}{1 + v/\eta c} \cong \frac{c}{\eta} + v\left(1 - \frac{1}{\eta^2}\right)$$

Problem 53. Using the *velocity transformation*, show that the speed of light in a vacuum is always c in special relativity.

Problem 54. Σ' moves in the $+x$ direction with respect to Σ. Clocks at the origin of Σ and Σ' are synchronized at $t = 0 = t' = x' = x$. At some later time the clock at the origin of Σ' comes next to a clock at a distance 1 in Σ. What are the readings of the clocks? Assume $\gamma = \frac{5}{4}$. The clocks in Σ are synchronized with respect to each other as are the clocks in Σ'. Also, construct the appropriate Minkowski diagram.

Answer: $\quad t = \dfrac{5}{3c} \qquad t' = \dfrac{t}{\gamma} = \dfrac{4}{3c}$

Problem 55. In ascribing the excess precession of the perihelion of mercury to general relativity, we must assume that we have calculated all the "Newtonian" effects. It can be shown, for example, that, if the equatorial diameter of the sun exceeds the polar diameter by .028 percent, the excess precession could be accounted for in a "Newtonian" way. The next two problems are really mechanics but are intended to show the student that it is unlikely that the solar diameters are as much different as would be required above.

Calculate the percentage difference between the polar and equatorial diameters of the earth, and compare with the measured values. This problem is a "calibration" because we can check our theoretical prediction with the known answer. Incidentally, this problem was first solved by Newton himself.

Problem 56. Apply the technique established in the previous problem to the sun to calculate $\Delta r/r$, and compare with the value required to explain the anomalous precession. The period of the solar rotation is 26 days.

Answer: Factor of 15 too small.

Problem 57. Using the expression $\Phi = 6\pi\alpha/a(1 - e^2)$, calculate the perihelion precession of mercury in one century. The semi-major axis $a = 58 \times 10^{11}$ cm, the eccentricity $e = .205$, the period is 88 days.

Answer: 42 sec/century.

Problem 58. Show that the average of the Doppler shift in the forward and backward directions leads to the second-order Doppler shift.

Problem 59. In Figure 33 (a) Calculate the theoretical curve shown, and
(b) Determine the first- and second-order Doppler shifts expected if the atoms have an energy of 6,780 ev. The wavelength of the spectral line is 4,861 Å.

Answer: (a) $\Delta\lambda_S = \Delta\lambda_F{}^2/9{,}722$. (b) $\Delta\lambda_S = .035\,\text{Å}$; $\Delta\lambda_F = 18.2\,\text{A}$.

Problem 60. A pendulum hangs at a place on the earth where the latitude is λ.

(a) Assuming that the direction of g is toward the center of the earth, show that the angle ϵ between the direction determined by the plumb bob and the direction to the center of the earth is given by

$$\epsilon = \frac{w^2 R \sin\lambda \cos\lambda}{g - w^2 R \cos^2\lambda}$$

(b) Calculate this angle for a latitude of 45°, ω = angular velocity of the earth, R = earth radius (see Fig. 34).

Answer: (b) $\epsilon = 5.6$ seconds of arc.

Problem 61. Show that $\dfrac{p\beta c}{T} = \dfrac{\dfrac{T}{m_0 c^2} + 2}{\dfrac{T}{m_0 c^2} + 1}$.

Problem 62. The clocks along the x and x' axes of the Σ and Σ' systems of special relativity move with respect to each other, but at any distance, clocks are lined up side by side. Do any of these read the same? If so, which ones?

Problem 63. One way to advance the reading of a clock with respect to another clock would be to take two identical clocks and lower one (from infinity) into a gravitational field. After leaving the clock there (where it runs slow), it could be pulled back out and compared with the stationary clock. Find the condition under which a clock runs slow by 10 per cent at the surface of a large astronomical body where, at the same time, the surface gravity does not exceed $g = 1{,}000$ cm/sec². Calculate the size of the astronomical body.

Answer: Radius of object is 9×10^{16} cm or $3/10\pi$ light years.

References

1. Max Born, *Einstein's Theory of Relativity*, London, Methuen, 1924.
2. A. S. Eddington, *Report on the Relativity of Gravitation*, London, Fleetway Press, 1920.
3. A. S. Eddington, *Space, Time and Gravitation*, Cambridge, England, Cambridge University Press, 1921; and Harper Torchbooks, New York, (paperbound), 1959.
4. A. Einstein, *The Meaning of Relativity*, Princeton, N.J., Princeton University Press, 1946.
5. A. Haas, *Introduction to Theoretical Physics*, New York, Van Nostrand, 1926, Vol. II.
6. G. Joos, *Theoretical Physics*, New York, Stechert, 1932.
7. R. Leighton, *Principles of Modern Physics*, New York, McGraw-Hill, 1959.
8. R. B. Lindsay and H. Margenau, *Foundations of Physics*, London, Wiley, 1936.
9. H. A. Lorentz, A. Einstein, H. Minkowski and H. Weyl, *The Principle of Relativity*, London, Methuen, 1923, and Dover Publications (paperbound).
10. G. C. McVittie, *Cosmological Theory*, London, Methuen, 1952.
11. G. C. McVittie, *General Relativity and Cosmology*, New York, Wiley, 1956.

12. C. Möller, *The Theory of Relativity*, Oxford, Oxford University Press, 1934.

13. W. Panofsky and M. Phillips, *Classical Electricity and Magnetism*, Reading, Mass., Addison-Wesley, 1955.

14. D. C. Peaslee, *Elements of Atomic Physics*, Englewood Cliffs, N.J., Prentice-Hall, 1955.

15. F. K. Richtmeyer, *Introduction to Modern Physics*, New York, McGraw-Hill, 1942.

16. A. Sommerfeld, *Electrodynamics*, New York, Academic Press, 1952.

17. R. C. Tolman, *The Theory of the Relativity of Motion*, Berkeley, University of California Press, 1917.

APPENDIX   Useful
Relativistic
Relations

Lorentz Transformation

$$x = \gamma(x' + \beta ct') \qquad x' = \gamma(x - \beta ct)$$
$$y = y' \qquad\qquad y' = y$$
$$z = z' \qquad\qquad z' = z$$
$$ct = \gamma(ct' + \beta x') \qquad ct' = \gamma(ct - \beta x)$$

where $\beta = \dfrac{v}{c}$ and $\gamma = \dfrac{1}{\sqrt{1 - \beta^2}}$

Time Dilatation

$$t = \gamma t' \qquad (x' = 0) \qquad t' \text{ is proper time in } \Sigma'$$
$$t' = \gamma t \qquad (x = 0) \qquad t \text{ is proper time in } \Sigma$$

Lorentz Contraction

$$x = \gamma x' \qquad (t' = 0) \qquad \text{measurement made in } \Sigma'$$
$$x' = \gamma x \qquad (t = 0) \qquad \text{measurement made in } \Sigma$$

Velocity Addition

$$v'_x = \frac{v_x - v}{1 - \frac{vv_x}{c^2}} \qquad v_x = \frac{v'_x + v}{1 + \frac{vv'_x}{c^2}}$$

$$v'_y = \frac{v_y}{\gamma\left(1 - \frac{vv_x}{c^2}\right)} \quad \text{and} \quad v_y = \frac{v'_y}{\gamma\left(1 + \frac{vv'_x}{c^2}\right)}$$

$$v'_z = \frac{v_z}{\gamma\left(1 - \frac{vv_x}{c^2}\right)} \qquad v_z = \frac{v'_z}{\gamma\left(1 + \frac{vv'_x}{c^2}\right)}$$

Relativistic Mass

$$m = \frac{m_0}{\sqrt{1 - \beta^2}} \qquad m_0 \text{ is rest mass}$$

Relativistic Kinetic Energy

$$T = m_0 c^2(\gamma - 1) = (m - m_0)c^2$$

Relativistic Total Energy

$$\mathcal{E} = mc^2 = \gamma m_0 c^2 = T + m_0 c^2$$

Relativistic Momentum

$$p = mv = \gamma \beta m_0 c$$

Rigidity

$$pc = 300 BR$$

Momentum and Energy

$$\mathcal{E}^2 = p^2 c^2 + m_0{}^2 c^4$$

The Trigonometric Substitution

$$\beta = \sin \Theta$$
$$p = m_0 c \tan \Theta$$
$$T = m_0 c^2 (\sec \Theta - 1)$$
$$w = m_0 c^2 \sec \Theta$$

The Relativistic Triangle

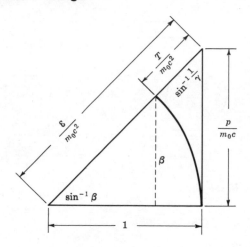

Transformation from Center of Mass to Lab

$$\beta_{CM} = \frac{\beta_L \gamma_L}{1 + \gamma_L} \quad \text{and} \quad 2\gamma_{CM}{}^2 = \gamma_L + 1$$

The Photon

$$m_0 = 0 \tag{a}$$

$$\mathcal{E} = h\nu = pc = mc^2 \tag{b}$$

$$p = \frac{h}{\lambda} \tag{c}$$

The Relativistic Doppler Shift

$$\nu = \nu'_0 \frac{(1 + \beta \cos \Theta')}{\sqrt{1 - \beta^2}} \quad \text{and} \quad \cos \Theta = \frac{\cos \Theta' + \beta}{1 + \beta \cos \Theta}$$

leads to

$$\nu_L = \nu_0 \frac{1 - \beta}{\sqrt{1 - \beta^2}} \cong \nu_0 \left(1 - \beta + \frac{1}{2} \beta^2\right)$$

Motion of recession (red shift)

$$\nu_L = \nu_0 \frac{1+\beta}{\sqrt{1-\beta^2}} \cong \nu_0 \left(1 + \beta + \frac{1}{2}\beta^2\right)$$

Motion of approach (blue shift)

$$\nu_T = \nu_0\sqrt{1-\beta^2} = \nu_0 \left(1 - \frac{1}{2}\beta^2\right)$$

Observed at right angles (red shift)

General Relativistic Transformation

Systems Σ, Σ', Σg

$$dr' = \frac{dx}{\gamma}$$

$$ds_\theta = dy$$

$$ds_\varphi = dz$$

$$dt' = \gamma\, dt$$

For $\Sigma \rightarrow \Sigma'$

$$\gamma = \frac{1}{\sqrt{1-\beta^2}}$$

For $\Sigma' \rightarrow \Sigma_g$

$$\gamma = \frac{1}{\left(1 - \dfrac{\alpha}{r}\right)} = 1 + \frac{\alpha}{r}$$

In a gravitational field

$$r \rightarrow r\left(1 - \frac{\alpha}{r}\right) \qquad \text{Radial length}$$

$$T \rightarrow T\left(1 + \frac{\alpha}{r}\right)$$

$$l \rightarrow l \qquad \text{Tangential length}$$

$$M \rightarrow M\left(1 + \frac{\alpha}{r}\right)$$

$$\alpha = \frac{GM}{c^2} = \text{gravitational radius}$$

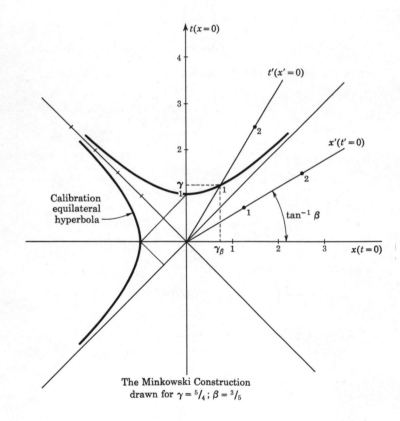

The Minkowski Construction
drawn for $\gamma = {}^5/_4$; $\beta = {}^3/_5$

INDEX